Assembly Stories from A   the world

Assembly Stories
from Around the World

William Dargue

Oxford University Press 1983

Oxford University Press, Walton Street, Oxford OX2 6DP

Oxford London Glasgow
New York Toronto Melbourne Auckland
Kuala Lumpur Singapore Hong Kong Tokyo
Delhi Bombay Calcutta Madras Karachi
Nairobi Dar es Salaam Cape Town

and associated companies in
Beirut Berlin Ibadan Mexico City Nicosia

Oxford is a trade mark of Oxford University Press
© William Dargue 1983
First published 1983

ISBN 0 19 917052 5

Filmset by Eta Services (Typesetters) Ltd., Beccles, Suffolk
Printed by Biddles Ltd., Guildford, Surrey

Contents

Christian Festivals

Hindu Festivals

Jewish Festivals

Introduction

All religions have a rich store of story material which is the heritage of us all. In the interests of mutual respect and understanding I want to make these stories from around the world available to teachers and children.

Each of the religions found in Britain follows an annual cycle of festivals into which is woven the story of its founders and heroes, its struggles, achievements and hopes. A festival is a symbolic re-enactment of the historical or mythological event whose inspiration and example is recalled as a spur to the faithful.

These stories represent ways in which the human race has tried to come to terms with the Infinite and with itself.

The Notes

Preceding each story is a short note on the celebration of the festival and some historical and cultural background to give it a context for teachers unfamiliar with the religion concerned. I have also indicated related stories and hope that these notes may direct those who wish to use this book as an RE resource to a wider area of study.

The Stories

All the stories are self-contained, with one or two clearly marked exceptions, and are designed to be read straight from the book. I have given a rough guide indicating how long it takes to read each story aloud.

The Quotations

After every story is a quotation from the relevant holy book or devotional literature which may be used as a prayer or pause for thought. I have adapted these passages from one or more translations into language that children can more easily understand. It is inevitable that difficult ideas will be expressed in difficult language; the problem with my approach is that simplification will lead, at best, to a loss of nuance and at worst to a loss of meaning. But as a teacher I prefer my children to grasp the essence of something simply expressed rather than to understand very little of one of the standard versions. Thus when I say a prayer is 'from' such-and-such a source, it means that I have *adapted* it from whatever sources I had (please see the Bibliography).

Religious Calendars

Each religion follows its own calendar, which does not move in line with the Gregorian calendar in general secular use throughout the world. Most religious calendars are luni-solar; that is, the months follow the cycle of the moon but the year itself is held in check within certain limits set by the solar year. There are further complications. The Christian calendar has some dates fixed in the solar year while others move according to a hypothetical moon. Some Orthodox Christian churches follow an earlier calendar and celebrate some festivals later than the Western churches. The Islamic calendar is entirely lunar and advances by 10–11 days annually according to the Gregorian. In addition, Buddhist, Hindu and Sikh traditions based on Indian calendars require an actual lunar sighting to determine the start of their festivals. By and large, therefore, it is useless to try and give very much indication other than a fairly broad span when the festival might occur: e.g. January/February.

However, I can heartily recommend the annually produced multi-faith festival calendar which does give precise dates for nearly all the festivals in this book and more besides:

Calendar of Religious Festivals
edited by Desmond F. Brennan for the SHAP Working Party
and published by the Commission for Racial Equality.
(See the Bibliography for more details, page 193.)

The Gregorian calendar counts its years from the supposed year of the birth of Jesus of Nazareth; years before are denoted by BC (Before Christ), years after by AD (Anno Domini – Latin for In the Year of Our Lord). The use of BC and AD are in effect professions of Christian faith. With due respect to members of other faiths, dates here are given as BCE – Before the Christian Era, and CE – of the Christian Era.

The Contents Lists

There are two lists of contents. The first lists the religions alphabetically, the festivals as they occur from January to December, and the stories associated with each festival. The second, printed as an appendix, also lists the stories by religion but in such an order as to give a continuous historical narrative. Not all the stories fit into this scheme and so not all of them appear in the second list of contents.

I have tried to tell all of these stories from the viewpoint of a member of the religion concerned. I have tried to present them as I have found them in my source material from the various faiths, not apologetically but with the positive conviction and self-assurance of faith. It is my sincere hope that I have succeeded in some measure and my hope too that this collection of stories will contribute in some way to greater knowledge and better understanding between people of all creeds and cultures in Britain.

Buddhist Festivals

The Day of the Death of the Buddha (Paranirvana Day)

February

Mahayana Buddhists (found in Tibet, Mongolia, China, Korea and Japan) celebrate the physical death of Lord Buddha today. He had attained enlightenment at the age of 35 but remained on earth teaching the way to enlightenment out of compassion to all who would listen. He died at the age of 80 in 483 BCE at Kusinagara (modern Kasia, Uttar Pradesh state, India) about 150 kilometres north-west of Patna. A week after his death his body was cremated in the manner reserved for royalty and the ashes were divided between the eight prominent clans of the region. The relics were buried under tall pagodas where they continue to receive veneration to this day.

Devadatta Tries to Kill the Buddha   (4 min)

Like most religious leaders Buddha had enemies. One of them was his own cousin, Devadatta, who disagreed with Buddha about the way that Buddhist monks should be organised. It is probable that there was a touch of jealousy in the things Devadatta did. Buddha always called his way of life 'the Middle Way'. He believed that too much luxury was a bad thing, but he also disagreed with the way in which some Indian monks tried to learn the truth. They had extremely strict rules. They weren't allowed to enjoy themselves at all, they could eat hardly anything, and they had to spend every minute sitting deep in thought. Buddha believed you could lead a life in the middle of these two ways, a life where you used your common-sense about following rules, where you didn't starve yourself, but where you weren't greedy either.

Devadatta thought that Buddha was being soft. He thought it was becoming too easy for people to be monks, and he argued with Buddha about it. In the end Devadatta decided that he would take some of Buddha's own people off with him and form a group of monks who would follow a lot of very strict rules.

'It's no good, Devadatta,' said the Buddha. 'If you make the rules too strict, people won't be able to follow them. My way of life is for ordinary people who want to understand. Besides, I tried starving myself and obeying strict rules like yours and that was not the way to the truth. Follow a middle way, cousin.'

But Devadatta took no notice. He went off in a bad temper.

Devadatta decided to kill his cousin, the Buddha. No one was going to follow Devadatta while Buddha was alive. It was the only thing to do.

Devadatta went to his friend, King Ajatasatru of Magadha. He was promised whatever help he needed. Devadatta chose a band of men from the King's guard and an ambush was laid. The group of soldiers hid themselves behind a huge wooden door where Buddha had to pass. As Buddha came towards them, they drew their swords ready for the kill. It should have been easy; there were many of them armed to the teeth, and he was only one, and carried no weapons at all. As Buddha came to the door his enemies sprang out with their swords raised ready to kill him. But Buddha spoke so calmly and gently to them that they felt ashamed and laid down their weapons. They had never before met a humble man who had so little fear. Devadatta sneaked away.

Another time Buddha and his friends were sitting at the foot of a high cliff. Devadatta had climbed up to the top and stood beside an enormous boulder which he intended to push down on them. He was determined to kill his cousin in any way that he could. With a mighty push Devadatta heaved the rock to the edge and watched it hurtle down towards the Buddha. The monks with Buddha scattered, shouting to him to move quickly. Buddha sat still and before it reached him the heavy stone split into two pieces, falling to either side of him.

Devadatta never succeeded in his plans to kill the Buddha. Indeed it is said that he came back to ask for the Buddha's forgiveness and was taken back as a monk not long before he died.

The Death of the Buddha   (4 min.)

Three months before the Buddha's eightieth birthday, the demon, Mara, came to tempt him for the last time. Mara told the Buddha that he should die happy now that he had found out the truth about life, and that he should leave the people on earth to sort out their own problems. To Mara's amazement Buddha this time agreed. He would leave the world and his body behind, and enter a state of perfect peacefulness in which there could be no more suffering or sorrow or unhappiness. Mara was delighted. He believed that the world would now fall into confusion without its great leader.

Buddha came to the small town of Kusinagara in the lower hills of the Himalaya mountains. He rested at a small Buddhist monastery where a few monks lived, in mud huts with straw roofs, ate very simple food and lived life just as Buddha had taught. Buddha was very satisfied. He had been on a long journey to visit all the little monasteries he had founded and they were all living the rules he had made. Mara, the demon, had lost again. Certainly Buddha was going to die, but the truth he had preached was in safe hands and would live for ever.

Buddha called his friends and disciples to him and told them that he was near to death. Their eyes filled with tears and many wept out loud. But Buddha told them: 'You must not weep for me. You knew I would have to leave you sooner or later. How many times have I told you that everything in the world changes? It is no use trying to hold on to things.'

Ananda, a cousin of Buddha and his most faithful disciple, prepared a place for Buddha to rest by the gently flowing waters of the River Hiranyavati. The trees round about were laden with heavy blossom and music floated on the breeze.

Buddha spoke: 'Listen, my disciples, everything in the world must die. A man must lose everything he loves. But do not say that you have no master when I am gone. Remember the words I have taught you: they are now your master.'

Then the Buddha lay down and began to meditate, to concentrate deeply. A short while later he stopped breathing and his body died. Buddha was now in nirvana. All suffering was at an end in a state of perfect rest and peace.

*

Before he died the Buddha made this famous speech:

'Be like an island. You must save yourself. No-one and nothing else can save you. Hold on to the truths I have taught you as an island. Hold on to the truth to save you. Do not look to anyone else to save you. Whoever is like an island and looks to no-one and nothing to save them, but holds fast to the truth to save them, they shall reach the highest heights.' (from the Maha-paranirvana Sutta, c.50 BCE)

The Birthday of Buddha Sakyamuni

March/April

This Mahayana Buddhist festival celebrates the birth in 563 BCE of the Buddha Siddhartha Gotama, who is often referred to as Sakyamuni, the Sage of the Sakya clan. Sakyamuni attained enlightenment, but chose to devote the rest of his natural life to teach mankind his doctrine. Theravada Buddhists (of Sri Lanka, Burma and Thailand) celebrate his birth on the full-moon day of Vesakha (q.v.).

In Japan images of the Buddha are bathed with an infusion of hydrangea leaves and surrounded with flowers. Processions are held where the priests scatter confetti in the shape of lotus flowers.

The Birth of Prince Siddhartha   (4 min.)

On the slopes of the Himalaya mountains, on the borders of India and Nepal, lived a rich young king, Suddhodana, and his beautiful wife, Queen Maya. Life was peaceful and good.

One night Queen Maya dreamed of a handsome white elephant which walked three times round her bed trumpeting as it went. The elephant came to her and entered her side. Next morning the King's wise men told her that the dream foretold that she would give birth to a baby boy who would be someone very special.

Not long before the baby was due, the Queen decided to visit her parents. She set out in her golden carriage, but before they had gone very far, she called to the driver to stop. The horses slowed and the golden carriage came to a halt in a beautiful clearing in the forest. Birds sang, wild animals darted to and fro, flowers bloomed and everything was full of peace. It was here that the baby was born. It was a boy as Queen Maya had learned from the dream and she called him Siddhartha which means 'A Wish Come True'.

The King called his wise men and priests together to foretell the baby prince's future. Some said that he could become a great emperor; but others said that he would become a poor and humble monk. The last of the priests to speak told the King that he would indeed become a monk, but a monk who would one day see the real truth of life, that he would show this truth to all men, and that he would become a buddha. When the prince saw four signs he would leave home to become a monk. The four signs were an old man, a sick man, a dead man, and a monk. King Suddhodana wanted his son to become a great emperor not a monk. He was determined to keep all sadness away from Prince Siddhartha.

As Siddhartha grew up the King made sure that he never saw sick or old people. Even dying flowers were picked from the royal gardens so that he would not see them. Death was never mentioned. King Suddhodana had three palaces built for his son, one for each season of the year (the hot season, the rainy season, and the cool season). Everything inside the Prince's palace was joy and excitement. The King made sure there were always plenty of people to visit him, plenty of games to play, and plenty of entertainment. He must never get bored, for if he was bored he would want to travel away from the palace and then he would be sure to see the sights he must not see – old age, illness, and death.

Siddhartha's Marriage   (4 min.)

Prince Siddhartha reached the age when he was expected to marry. His father, King Suddhodana, announced to all the lands around that a ceremony was to be held at which wonderful gifts would be presented to all the girls who came. This was so that his son, Siddhartha, could see the most beautiful girls and choose one to be his wife. Hundreds of girls arrived at the palace on the day and the presents were given out, but Siddhartha did not take much notice. When all the jewels and golden necklaces and silver brooches had been distributed there arrived at the court a girl called Yasodhara. She was the daughter of one of the King's ministers and had not thought that Siddhartha would want to see her. Her father had persuaded her to attend but she had arrived too late to be given a present. Prince Siddhartha went up to her, took the most valuable ring from his own finger, and slipped it on to hers. The King knew who his son had chosen.

Now it was the custom of the land of King Suddhodana that a man to be married must prove himself the best of all those men who wanted to marry a particular girl. This was done in competitions of sport, shooting arrows, sword fighting, and horse and chariot racing. Even Prince Siddhartha would have to enter such a competition to win Yasodhara as his new wife. The King was worried. Although Siddhartha had had plenty of practice, he had only ever played sports and competitions at the palace. The King was anxious in case any of the other men who wanted to win the beautiful Yasodhara might prove to be better than his son. He need not have been concerned. Siddhartha easily beat all who tried to play against him. What was more, when a great bow was brought that had belonged to the King's ancestors, a bow so mighty no-one had ever managed to shoot with it, Siddhartha not only managed to pull it back and fit an arrow, he placed the arrow right in the centre of the target.

With great happiness and rejoicing, people came from all over the land and

from countries far away to join in the celebrations at the marriage of Prince
Siddhartha and Yasodhara.

When Yasodhara gave birth to a son, Rahula, King Suddhodana was as
happy as he could be – Siddhartha would not leave to be a monk now, whether
or not he saw the sights of illness, old age, and death. He would not leave
his own family behind.

Siddhartha Leaves Home   (4 min.)

Siddhartha began to get bored with the life of luxury at the palace. He was
curious to see what lay outside its walls. He called Channa, his chariot-driver,
to take him out of the palace, into the streets of the town. Suddenly the Prince
called Channa to stop. He had seen a man whose hair was white, whose skin
was wrinkled, and whose back and legs were bent. Siddhartha had never seen
old age before and asked Channa what was the matter with the man. He was
shocked to hear that everyone grew old, that his beautiful young wife would
grow old, that his baby son would grow old, and that he himself would grow
old.

On another day Siddhartha asked Channa to take him into the town where
he saw a man so weak he could not stand. The man's face was covered with
sores and he cried out in pain. Siddhartha had never seen anyone ill before.
He was shocked to learn that anyone could become ill, at any time, and there
was very little that could be done about it. Even a prince like Siddhartha
could become ill.

On yet another visit to the town Siddhartha saw a group of people unhappy
and crying. They were carrying a man. Channa explained that the man being
carried was dead, that everyone who is born will die, that all of Siddhartha's
family and friends were sure to die, that Siddhartha himself was bound to die,
and that there was certainly nothing that could be done about it. The Prince
was so shocked by this that he felt ill and told Channa to take him home
immediately.

On the way back to the palace Siddhartha saw a fourth sight that he had
never seen before. It was a man with a shaved head wearing a yellow robe.
Channa told the Prince that this man was a monk – a man who had given up
owning things, who had given up his family and home and friends, and who
had set out to find a way to end suffering. Siddhartha noticed how peaceful
the monk's face looked, how calm he seemed to be.

The life at the palace meant nothing to Siddhartha now. He had seen the
four signs the priest had foretold – old age, sickness, death, and a monk. And
he could not stop thinking about the sad truth of being alive. He decided that
he had led an empty wasteful life so far and that he must try to find peace in
the same way as the monk had found peace.

One night as the palace lay in sleep Siddhartha called Channa to saddle horses and to ride out of the palace with him. The Prince did not want to say goodbye to his family because they would be sure to stop him from going. But before he left he could not resist one last look at his sleeping wife and baby son. He did not even dare to kiss them for fear of waking them up. He knew he had to begin his journey and quietly he rode out of the palace.

Channa and Siddhartha rode until they reached the River Neranjara. Here the Prince cut off his long princely hair and gave his royal clothes and expensive jewellery to Channa to take back to the King. Channa was to tell the King not to worry and not to be sad, for Siddhartha would return when he had learned the truth he was looking for. Sadly Channa left him.

And so Siddhartha who had been a prince, set off with nothing, with no family or riches, wearing only the robe of a wandering monk. He had nothing and he wanted nothing except to understand the reasons for suffering and unhappiness and how to cure them. It was a journey in search of truth.

*

Many years later Siddhartha came to understand the suffering of the world and preached his message to everyone. On one occasion he spoke to a group of fire-worshippers:

'The whole world is in flames. What is it that keeps the fire burning? The fire is kept alive by wanting, by hatred and ignorance, by birth, old age and death, by weeping and sorrow, and by grief and despair. So the wise man does not hold on to these things and in this way the causes of suffering are removed from his heart.' (from The Fire Sermon)

Vesakha Celebration (Vesakha Puja)

Full-moon day of the month of Vesakha
April/May

This Theravada Buddhist festival is celebrated in Sri Lanka, Burma, and Thailand as the day of the birth of Gotama Buddha in 563 BCE, the day of his enlightenment which occurred 35 years later to the day, and also of his death 45 years later, again on the same day. Houses are decorated with flowers, garlands, and lights, as are temples and statues of the Buddha. Charitable gifts are made in memory of the Buddha's concern for mankind, and caged birds may be freed

*in memory of his concern for all living things. Mahayana Buddhists celebrate
these festivals on different occasions (see The Day of Enlightenment, the Death
of Buddha and The Birthday of Buddha Sakyamuni).*

Buddha, the Enlightened One   (6 min.)

Prince Siddhartha Gotama was born about 2,500 years ago in a little kingdom
on the borders of Nepal and India. He had left the royal palace and a life of
luxury, and had set out to find the truth of life. He had been shocked when he
realised that all living things grow old and die and that there is much suffering
and pain through disease. He wanted to find out if there was a way to
overcome these sorrows.

Siddhartha joined a group of monks who had also given up everything to
find out about truth. They starved their bodies and lived uncomfortable lives
in order to concentrate their minds. For six hard years Siddhartha did the
same, but he only found that starving himself confused and clouded his mind
instead of making things clearer. He came no nearer to understanding the
truth.

When Siddhartha told the monks that he was going to eat again they left
him in disgust and disappointment.

Siddhartha continued his journey alone. Into the forest he went. And as he
walked he thought. The life of luxury and plenty at the palace had not been
right. Neither had it been right to starve himself. There must be another way –
a middle way. He sat down in the shade of a fig tree and decided that there he
would stay until he was able to work out the right answer to his problem.

Mara, the demon tempter, had heard of the Prince's efforts to seek out the
truth at all costs. He decided to pay Siddhartha a visit. First Mara sent his
three beautiful daughters to tempt Siddhartha back to the world. Beautiful
they were, gracefully they danced and sweetly they sang, but, though
Siddhartha could see them and hear the things they offered him, he sat deep in
thought and took no notice. Then the demon, Mara, sent armies of his
hideous creatures against the Prince – a monster with a thousand mouths
bristling with angry teeth, demons drinking blood or eating snakes, demons
ugly and misshapen, devils shrieking fearful screams and brandishing wicked
swords and spears. But as they approached Siddhartha, their cries grew silent
and they found they were unable to move. They retreated back to the
underworld in defeat.

Mara knew that he would have to try and defeat Siddhartha himself. He
could not allow the Prince to find out the truth of life and save mankind. The
devil stood before Siddhartha, who showed no sign of even seeing him. The
demon took out his most mighty weapon, a steel disc with the power of a

thunderbolt, a weapon with which he had split mountains in two. Tightening every muscle and using every last bit of his strength he hurled the steel disc at Siddhartha's head. It shot through the air, spinning – but as it came near the Prince, it turned into a garland of flowers and hung in mid-air over Siddhartha's head.

Meanwhile, the truth was coming to Siddhartha. He was beginning to see the light, beginning to understand the way the world worked, and the way men could be saved. He was becoming the Buddha, the One who has seen the Light.

Buddha remembered all the lives he had lived and saw how the bad things continued into later lives and how the good things continued. He saw that this happened to every living thing – the evil they did would come back to them perhaps in another life, while the good they did would always be with them. He saw that it was no use trying to find real happiness for the soul on earth. It is no use trying to hold on to the things in the world because everything changes; people, seasons, friendships, mountains, seas. Even the earth itself will one day be destroyed. In order to find peace all living things must escape from the changing world.

Buddha understood that there are four truths about life. The first is that the world is full of suffering – illness, old age, losing those you love, not getting the things you want. The second truth is that this suffering is caused by wanting things you can't have: in other words suffering is caused by greed and selfishness. Thirdly, the way to end suffering is to end selfishness. And the last truth is that of the Middle Way, the way that selfishness and greed are overcome – you must behave in a truthful way and you must meditate. From this will come wisdom and understanding. From this will come peace.

As Mara watched he seemed to see a light surround the Buddha. Slowly the sun came up and the full moon of night faded. As the sun rose, so the Buddha's eyes fixed on the demon, Mara. The Buddha touched the ground with one finger and Mara sank to his knees and bowed before the man who had conquered the universe.

Devadatta Tries to Kill the Buddha (3 min.)

Devadatta had often plotted with his friend, King Ajatasatru, to kill Buddha. Ajatasatru was a selfish man; to become king he had put his own father in prison. And Devadatta was like him; he was jealous of the power the Buddha had over people.

Devadatta arranged with the King to have one of the great royal elephants made drunk. Fiery spirit liquor was forced down its throat and the poor animal began to stagger about upset and confused. The guards dragged the swaying animal to the gates of the elephant house and then threw open the doors. The huge beast stood unsteadily for a moment, then screamed out in fear and anger and began to charge down the street towards the market place.

Of course, Devadatta knew that Buddha and his friends had just left the market place. They were walking right into the path of the maddened elephant.

The elephant charged on in a frightened rage. It trampled several people to death, it overturned and smashed a number of carriages, it even demolished the fronts of one or two small houses. People dashed away, shouting to clear the streets. Buddha's disciples heard the noise and tried to pull the Buddha to one side. He refused, and continued to walk calmly up the street towards the elephant. As he walked a small girl ran out into the elephant's path. The animal did not stop. It hurled itself straight towards the little child. In a voice that could be heard above the furious trumpeting of the drunken animal, Buddha shouted:

'Stop! You have been sent to kill me, not that child. She has done you no harm.'

And when the elephant heard the Buddha's calm commanding voice, full of love and kindness, it stopped, slowly walked towards him and knelt down, laying its head on the ground at the Buddha's feet.

Devadatta had been hiding, waiting to see the Buddha killed. Ashamed and angry he fled. Not long after this Devadatta himself grew ill and it is said that as he died, he called on the Buddha's help.

Assalayana Tries to Catch the Buddha out   (4 min.)

In Buddha's time there were four classes of people in India. The highest was the class of the priests. Children born into the priest class did not *have* to become priests, but nobody could become a priest who was not born into this class. The next was the warrior class to which the kings and nobles belonged, then the merchant class, and lastly the working class. There was a class of people even lower than all of these, so low they weren't even called a class; they were simply called the untouchables.

Buddha taught that it was the type of life you lived that was important and not whether you were born in the highest class, or whether you were rich or well-educated. And, of course, this teaching upset people – especially the rich and well-educated.

Assalayana was of a very high class. He asked Buddha:

'The high class say that they are the only good class. Is it not true that they were born out of the mouth of God?'

'Do the high class really think that?' asked Buddha. 'Aren't they born of women like everyone else? And tell me – is it true that when a lower class thief or murderer or sinner dies, his soul flies straight to hell; if he's high class, he goes to heaven?'

'On no,' replied Assalayana. 'The wicked go to hell whatever class they're from.'

'And can only high class men go down to the river to wash off the dust and dirt, and not the people of the lower classes?'

'Well, no, anyone can do that. It doesn't matter what class they're from.'

'Listen,' said the Buddha. 'Suppose that there are two brothers from the highest class. One of them is intelligent and well-educated; the other knows nothing and is completely uneducated. Which one would you serve first at a meal in your house. The educated or the uneducated one?'

'The educated one, of course,' answered Assalayana. 'There's no point in serving the uneducated brother.'

'Yes, but what if the educated man is wicked and sinful, and the uneducated one is kind and good?'

'In that case, I'd serve the uneducated one. There's no serving a wicked man in my house.'

The Buddha smiled and said:

'First, Assalayana, you said that the important thing was the class you were born into; then you said it was whether you were educated or not; and now you have just decided that it is whether you are good or bad that is the most important. I think you must agree with me now: the class you come from is unimportant, your education is unimportant – what matters is the type of life you lead – good or bad.'

Assalayana sat silent and said nothing.

*

The Buddha said:

'If a man talks a lot about the teaching I have given, but does not follow any of it, he is like a cowherd counting somebody else's cows. He is no disciple of the Buddha. But if a man knows only a little bit of my teaching, and carries out the things I have taught – if he gets rid of his selfishness and hatred, if he fills his mind with knowledge and calmness and does not try to hang on to the things of the world, then he is a disciple of the Buddha.' (from the Dhammapada, c.50 BCE)

Poson

Full-moon of June

This Theravada Buddhist festival celebrates the spread of Buddhism and its growth to a world religion. King Asoka (ruled c.273–232 BCE) gradually extended his kingdom by conquest until it covered all of the Indian subcontinent except for the craggy mountainous region towards the south. Revolted by the horrors of war he turned to Buddhism. Thereafter he ruled his empire by the force of his personality rather than by the sword. His missions on behalf of the faith were sent to all parts of India, to Syria, Egypt and Macedonia, and most important to Sri Lanka, which today has the longest lived tradition of any Buddhist country. From there Buddhism spread eastwards to the countries of central, eastern, and south-east Asia where it is still predominant. There are now perhaps 250,000,000 adherents of Mahayana Buddhism (the Northern school) and 50,000,000 Theravadins (the Southern school).

A Small Boy's Gift   (4 min.)

A small boy in India had heard that a famous teacher and religious leader was coming to his village. The man was Gotama Buddha. The day arrived and the whole of the village turned out to see and hear what the great man had to say. As he came along the dusty road the small boy could see him, dressed very simply, but walking with an air of great peace and calmness. With him were a number of monks dressed in yellow robes.

The Buddha sat down in the shade of some trees at the centre of the little village and the monks sat with him. And he began to speak. He told the people that they could be saved if they lived a simple life without greed and selfishness; he told them that there were simple rules to follow. If they did not follow these rules, if they lived lives of greed and thought only of themselves, then they would continue to be born and reborn and born again for ever.

The villagers listened. When he had finished the Buddha answered their questions patiently.

'I suppose you get to heaven quicker if you're from the high class and not working class like us?' asked one man.'

'Oh no,' answered the Buddha. 'What class you come from has nothing to do with anything. The good you do will decide how quickly you will find peace.'

'But how can we ignorant villagers remember all you have taught us? The priest is always moaning at us because we can't remember the words of his prayers and he calls us stupid because we don't understand them.'

'It doesn't matter how clever or how well-educated you are,' the Buddha replied. 'You don't have to remember all I have taught you. You just have to live the way I have shown you.'

'Should we pray to the gods to help us as the priest says?' asked another villager.

'Gods can't save you,' said Buddha. 'The good things and the selfish things you have done decide what will happen to you. Only you can save yourself.'

When he had finished speaking the people of the village went to their homes to find food and drink for the Buddha and his friends. Everyone brought something, no matter how small, and Buddha and the monks thanked them all kindly. Only the small boy had nothing to give. Tiny as he was he wanted to give something. He stooped down and scooped up some of the white sand which covered the ground all around the village. He offered it to Buddha. Buddha understood what the child was trying to say and smiled kindly at the little boy.

In a future life this little boy became the great King Asoka, Emperor of all India.

King Asoka Becomes a Buddhist   (5 min.)

Asoka's grandfather, King Chandragupta, had conquered a large part of India. Asoka's father had conquered still more. And now Asoka was busy trying to conquer the rest. He was determined to be king over all of India and not just over part of it.

King Asoka sent his troops to conquer one of the few parts of India still free – the country of Kalinga on the coast near Madras. Hundreds of soldiers had marched south through India stealing food from the poor villages, killing the people if they tried to stop them, and burning their houses. The might of Asoka's great Indian empire was then thrown against this tiny country of Kalinga. The Kalingan armies were wiped out and the soldiers of Asoka ran riot through the land, burning and stealing and killing.

King Asoka should have been pleased. He had captured one more piece of India and there was very little else left worth capturing. He should have been pleased. He had always been delighted with victories before and had held great feasts to celebrate them. But this time Asoka had seen the killing. He had been there when the two armies met. He had seen ordinary men stab and knife each other to death. He had seen ordinary men shoot arrows at each other. He had seen men hacking at each other with swords. He had seen the mighty, royal elephants trample men to death and he had seen the elephants fall and scream in pain as their legs were chopped at by the enemy. He had seen more blood than he could measure; he had seen men wounded and dying; he had seen wives and children searching among the dead to find their husbands and fathers. And he knew that all this had happened because he, the King, had ordered it.

His eyes filled with tears, his heart filled with sadness and he felt deeply ashamed and angry when he thought of all the other battles his men had fought at his command. He tried to think of the thousands and thousands of dead men, and the thousands and thousands of wives and children who had no husbands and fathers because of him. He thought of all the tiny villages where people had starved because his men had stolen their last bit of food. There was nothing he could do about the evil things he had done in the past – but he could make sure that nothing like it ever happened again.

He decided to become a Buddhist. Buddhists, he knew, did not believe in violence and fighting – they believed that all living things were precious. Asoka become a Buddhist.

Asoka learned all he could about the teaching of Buddha and brought Buddhist monks to his palace to teach the nobles. He did not force anyone to be a Buddhist; he hoped they would want to follow Buddha's teaching because they sincerely believed. And many did. As the years went by thousands of people all over India became Buddhists. Asoka sent Buddhist monks all over India so they could learn about the Buddha's teachings. He also sent missionaries to many foreign countries far and near, some of which also later became Buddhist.

Many centuries after Asoka died Buddhism died out altogether in India. But Asoka's work is not forgotten. Many countries today remember thankfully that he sent Buddhist missionaries to them and such countries as Sri Lanka and Thailand are strongly Buddhist today. As for Asoka – he is remembered as perhaps the only king in history who really did rule by love and not by the sword.

*

The Buddha often taught that love for all living things is one of the most important ways of reaching nirvana, the peace that comes with the ending of selfishness and suffering:

'As a mother cares for her son all her days, so a man's mind must be full of loving-kindness to all living things everywhere. He should fill the whole wide world with love and kindness and joy – above, below, around and everywhere, far-reaching, great, too big to measure, and free from the smallest trace of anger or hate.' (from the Sutta Nipata)

'Never in this world is hate stopped by hate – only by loving-kindness can hate be conquered.' (from the Dhammapada)

The Day of the Turning of the Wheel of the Law
(Dhammacakka Day)

Full-moon day of the month of Srvana
July/August

After attaining enlightenment and becoming himself a Buddha, Prince Siddhartha Gotama could have kept his knowledge and understanding to himself, but out of compassion for all living things he decided to teach the truth for the benefit of others. The Buddha (the Enlightened One) was born of royal parents in 563 BCE and died in 483 BCE in north-east India; he attained enlightenment on his 35th birthday and died on his 80th birthday, according to Theravada Buddhist tradition, on the full-moon of the month of Vesakha (q.v.). Dhammacakka Day is a Theravada Buddhist festival celebrated chiefly in Sri Lanka and south-east Asia and commemorates the preaching of the Buddha's first sermon at Benares (now Varanasi, Uttar Pradesh state).

The Buddha and the Five Hermits　　(6 min.)

Prince Siddhartha Gotama had realised that a life of luxury was not the life for him. He had been very comfortable living in his royal palace, but in his heart he searched for something more important than just being comfortable. Secretly Siddhartha left home – he left his father and mother, his wife and son and the luxuries he had been used to and set out to try and find the meaning of life.

Siddhartha gave away all the things he owned, even the good clothes he wore; he cut off his long princely hair and went to join a hermitage. At the hermitage were other men who were searching just as Siddhartha was. As Indians still do today, they had given up their homes and families and all the things that make life comfortable; they ate as little as possible and concentrated on trying to bring their minds nearer to God. Siddhartha too gave up these things – he even gave up his first name and was just called Gotama in order to try and forget himself and come nearer to the truth in his mind. But it was no use so Gotama tried several religious teachers, but none of them seemed to be able to teach him anything.

At last Gotama decided that he must try by himself and he came to the edge of a river where he sat down to meditate, to think. He sat crosslegged by the river, deep in thought. Each day he ate nothing but a few leaves or berries and he drank nothing but the water of the river. As time went by Gotama grew thinner and thinner until nothing remained of his body but a skeleton covered with skin. It was here that the five hermits found him.

They were amazed at his strength of mind. Here he was, eating virtually nothing at all, meditating on the truth of life; here was a man they could follow as their leader. They sat down beside him on the bank of the river and waited for him to tell them his message. They only ate when he ate; they only drank when he drank; they became as thin as he was. But he told them nothing. Gotama had learned nothing from starving himself.

One day Gotama went into the waters of the river to bathe. His body was so weak that he could hardly stand, and when the time came for him to climb the bank to get out he found he could hardly manage it. He was so thin that his muscles had almost disappeared and he was only able to haul himself out of the river by pulling with all his might on the branch of an overhanging tree. A girl from a nearby village had often seen Gotama sitting in meditation, and when she passed by the next day she realised that he would have to eat properly or very soon he would die. A little while later she returned with a bowl of rice for him. She had to feed him for he had not the strength to feed himself.

When the five hermits saw Gotama eating they were disgusted with him. They thought that his strength of mind had weakened, that he had become frightened of the uncomfortable life he was leading. They had followed him for nearly six years and now they felt that he had let them down. In disgust they left him.

Gotama had not learned the meaning of life through starvation, but he had learned something. He had found out that starving the body does not leave the mind free. It confuses the mind. Gotama had tried luxurious living and had not been satisfied; he had tried living with nothing at all and this had been no better. But he knew there must be an answer. He travelled on until he came to a certain fig tree. Here he sat down cross-legged and vowed that he would never move from the place until he had understood the truth he was searching for.

And throughout the day and throughout the night as the full moon shone on him Gotama sat deep in thought. By morning he had the answer, he had become enlightened, he had become a Buddha.

Gotama understood that all living things are born and reborn and that the things they do, good or bad, affect the happiness or unhappiness in their lives to come. People are unhappy because they do not understand this, because they try to have what they cannot have. It is only by understanding this, by not always worrying about selfish wants that suffering can be ended. Buddha realised that loving behaviour towards other living beings, and careful thinking, will lead to an understanding which will eventually become the ending of all suffering and the coming of peace.

Gotama's journey in search of truth was ended.

The Buddha's First Sermon   (6 min.)

Gotama had found the meaning of life. Sitting under the fig tree he had seen the light. He had become enlightened. Gotama became known as the Buddha, the Enlightened One, while the fig tree became known as the bodhi tree, the tree of enlightenment. Buddha sat beneath the bodhi tree for seven days, his mind completely at rest. It was the deepest feeling of calm that he had even known and he could have stayed there for ever.

While the Buddha sat there with nothing in his mind except for this wonderful peace, Mara, the demon came to tempt him:

'Why don't you stay like this for ever, Gotama? Instead of going back to the worries of the world, you could feel calm and peaceful for ever more.'

Buddha thought about this. After all this was what he had spent years of his life searching for.

'Yes, I think I will,' said Buddha. 'But perhaps I should go back into the world to preach my message to everyone, so that they can find peace too.'

The demon laughed:

'Do you really think they would listen to you? Even if they listened to you, do you think they would understand what you were talking about?'

Buddha knew this was true:

'I know you're right, Mara. But don't tempt me any more. I have decided that this is my job. I haven't lived many lives to find enlightenment and peace for myself alone. I must go out into the world and preach, whether the people want to hear or not, whether they understand or not.'

Nothing that Mara could do or say could now change the Buddha's mind.

*

Where was the Buddha to start telling the world about the truths he had discovered? He remembered the five hermits he had lived with for so long. They had been disgusted and disappointed when he had taken food and given up the hard and lonely life with them. Perhaps Buddha felt that he owed it to them to let them be the first to hear what he now had to say. He travelled on and found the hermits in the Deer Park at Benares. They were just as thin as when he had left them – and they didn't look any happier.

When they saw him coming, some of them laughed at him because he had given up their hard life and they thought he was soft. Others were angry with him for having the cheek to come back. But as the Buddha approached they could tell there was something different about him. He walked with a great calmness, there was great confidence in his eyes as he looked at them, and a great light seemed to surround him. They stopped what they were doing and fell quiet to hear what he had to say.

As the Buddha spoke, they soon realised that he had found what he had been searching for, and what they had been searching for. They bowed low and some of them fell on their knees when they heard the Buddha's words:

'It's no good living for fun and pleasure; it's no good either starving and torturing your body; the best way is the Middle Way. There are Four Holy Truths which you must learn if you are to find peace. The first is that there will always be suffering in life; you may find some happiness but it won't last long, and there will always be the sadness of death, there will be illness and disease, there will be arguments between friends. The second truth is that suffering is caused by greed, by bothering so much about ourselves, by wanting to hold on to things that are always changing. The third truth is that suffering can be overcome by getting rid of greed and selfishness. The fourth truth is the way to do this. By loving all living things, by living a useful life, by understanding yourself, you can escape the suffering of life. Eventually you will see the light, as I have done and you will also become a buddha.'

The five hermits knew this was the truth they heard and they became the first Buddhists.

King Ajatasatru Becomes a Buddhist   (4 min.)

Prince Ajatasatru was a friend of Buddha's cousin, Devadatta. It may have been jealousy that made Devadatta hate the Buddha, but then many of the things Devadatta did were selfish and rather nasty. Prince Ajatasatru was a grown man and his father, the King, seemed as if he was going to live for ever. Devadatta suggested to the prince that he shouldn't put up with this. Surely he wanted to be king while he was still young enough to enjoy it? This gave Ajatasatru an idea, and it wasn't long before the King found himself locked up in prison. His son crowned himself King Ajatasatru.

On a number of occasions Ajatasatru helped Devadatta try to kill Buddha, but their plans never worked. Although he was now king and had all that he wanted, Ajatasatru wasn't happy. He was often ill, though there never seemed to be any reason for his illness. His doctor, Jivaka, could do nothing.

At last Ajatasatru called Jivaka to him and demanded to know the truth.

'I know you have been frightened to tell me all you know,' said the King. 'You are frightened of what I might do to you if you did. I promise that no harm will come to you, if you will only tell me the truth. What is wrong with me?'

Jivaka answered honestly:

'There is nothing wrong with your body, Your Majesty. It is your mind that is ill — and that I cannot cure.'

'Is there no help for me?' asked the King.

'Only one man can help you – the Buddha.'

'Then you must take me to him,' answered the King.

Jivaka took his master to a clearing in the forest. There were no signs that anyone lived here. The grass was not trampled and the birds all sang. The King asked where the Buddha was. He had heard that he was here with a number of his disciples.

'Yes, Your Majesty,' replied Jivaka. 'He is here with twelve hundred followers.'

'What?' shouted the King. 'Is this a trap?'

'You must trust me, Master.'

Ajatasatru went on and saw, sitting in a clearing in the forest, twelve hundred people who had all come to hear the Buddha speak. There was not a sound. All ears were on the Buddha's words.

Ajatasatru sat and listened with the others and began to understand why his life was so miserable. The more he listened the more he was sure he understood the Four Holy Truths and the way to save himself. By the time the Buddha had finished speaking Ajatasatru himself had become a Buddhist.

*

Here is part of that first sermon that Buddha gave in the Deer Park. It is known to Buddhists as the Turning of the Wheel of the Law:

'This is the Holy Truth of Suffering:
birth is suffering, growing old is suffering, illness is suffering, death is suffering; it is suffering to love things that are worthless, it is suffering to lose things you love, it is suffering not to have what you want.

'This is the Holy Truth of how Suffering begins:
it comes from wanting things, things to delight and please you, wanting pleasure, wanting riches.

'This is the Holy Truth of the Ending of Suffering:
it is to stop wanting things completely, it is to be free of wanting.

'This is the Holy Truth of the Way to end Suffering:
it is the Eightfold Way: right understanding and thinking, right speaking, right behaviour, and right work, right effort, right mindfulness and right concentration.'

(from the Dhammacakka-ppavattana Sutta, c.50 BCE)

The Day of Enlightenment (Bodhi Day)

November/December

This is a Mahayana Buddhist festival and as such is celebrated in Japan, Korea, China, and central Asia where this sect is dominant. Theravada Buddhists celebrate the attainment of buddhahood of Prince Siddhartha Gotama in the month of Vesakha (q.v.). Mahayana Buddhists accept later scriptures than those attributed to the Buddha himself and the practice of their faith has probably been influenced more than Theravada Buddhism by indigenous popular beliefs. Buddha was born the son of King Suddhodana whose small prosperous country lay in the Himalayan foothills, the capital Kapilavastu being about 150 km east of Katmandu, Nepal. He was born 563 BCE, attained enlightenment at the age of 35 and died at 80 having established the basis for the spread of the faith he had developed. The Buddha attained nirvana, a state of extinction of the earthly desires that cause suffering; this would have been sufficient but out of compassion for all other living beings he chose to teach the way of salvation. Only by understanding the Four Noble Truths which set out the cause of suffering and by following the Eightfold Path of right thoughts and behaviour can the endless cycle of rebirth be escaped. This applies to all living beings including the gods.

The Young Prince Siddhartha   (7 min.)

Prince Siddhartha had everything. His father was the king of a very rich little kingdom at the foot of the Himalaya mountains. At his birth King Suddhodana had called the wise man, Asita, to come and foretell the baby's future. Asita examined the child carefully and when he had finished tears filled his old eyes.

'Why are you crying?' asked the King. 'What is wrong?'

'This child will grow up to be either a great saint or a king of the world. My tears are because I shall not live to hear what he will have to say.'

        *

As a young prince Siddhartha lived a life of ease and luxury. But he was shocked when he saw and understood that people grow ill, grow old, and die. He realised that there must be a way to overcome this suffering and set out into the world without a penny of his own and with only the yellow robe of a monk to wear.

He tried starving his body of food as many Indian monks do, in order to concentrate his mind on the problem of suffering. He became as thin as a skeleton but found that this did not give him the answer. And so he decided that there must be a way between luxury and starvation, a middle way to the truth.

As he sat under a fig tree throughout the night of the full moon in May, he concentrated his thoughts until at last his mind became clear. He understood that suffering is caused by wanting and that it can only be overcome by not wanting. As he understood these truths he became the Buddha, the Enlightened One.

Buddha was perfectly at peace and could have remained sitting there calmly and quietly, free from suffering. But he felt such a love for the world that he knew he would have to preach his message to all people.

He travelled for many years in northern India preaching his message. He taught that by following a simple life, by loving all living things, by working hard and concentrating on the problem, one could at last come to see the truth as he had himself seen, and so be set free.

At last he decided to visit the royal palace of his father, King Suddhodana. He travelled through India northwards towards the Himalayas and finally approached the capital city, Kapilavastu. The news that he was coming travelled faster and messengers came to the King bringing news of his famous son's return. The King wanted very much to see Siddhartha. He was now an old man and, before he died, he wanted to hear what his son had learnt.

When Siddhartha, the Buddha, reached Kapilavastu he refused to stay in the palace because he had sworn to avoid luxury. His father came to the clearing in the forest where Buddha and his friends were camped.

'I am old, Siddhartha. Won't you be king after I am dead?'

'No,' said Buddha. 'I have chosen to live of life of poverty and peace. I do not want the power and money that being a king brings.'

The next day the King's messengers brought news that Buddha and his friends were going round the city asking for food, begging like poor people. The King went to his son:

'Siddhartha, you don't need to beg. I have everything you need at the royal palace.'

'But it is the custom of monks to beg, Father.'

'You are descended from an ancient line of noble kings!'

'You are descended from kings, Father; I am descended from Buddhas who have lived and died to show men the way to true happiness.'

After hearing Buddha's teaching King Suddhodana became a follower of his son, and so did his cousin, his brother, and his nephew. Buddha went to see his wife, who was still upset after all these years that Buddha had left her to follow the path he had chosen. When Buddha came to her she would not talk to him, but sent her son, Rahula, to Buddha to claim his inheritance. As

Buddha had been a royal prince she expected him to give Rahula money and land and power.

'You can have all I have to give,' answered Buddha. 'You can hear my teaching and you can become one of my followers.'

Rahula did join the Buddha's disciples and is now remembered for being one of the most faithful.

*

Buddha said that it was no use praying to gods for help; every living thing must find the answer to its own problem of suffering by following the path that the Buddha had shown. So the following words are not prayers but promises which Buddhists make to themselves at least once a day.

Honour to the Blessed One, the Perfect One, the Enlightened Buddha!

I go to the Buddha for safety;
I go to the Teaching of the Buddha for safety;
I go to the Buddhist Monks for safety.

Again I go to the Buddha for safety;
Again I go to his Teaching for safety;
Again I go to the Monks for safety.

A third time I go to the Buddha for safety;
A third time I go to the Teaching for safety;
A third time I go to the Monks for safety.

(The Triple Gem or Refuge Formula)

I promise to hurt no living thing.
I promise not to steal.
I promise to be faithful to the one I married.
I promise not to tell lies.
I promise not to take drink, or drugs which will dull my brain.

(The Pancha Sila, The Five Precepts)

Chinese Festivals

New Year

1st of the first
January/February

This is the most important Chinese festival of the lunar year. It is a family festival of great merriment. There are special meals, the giving of presents, and visits to friends and relations. New paper pictures of the Kitchen God and the Guardians of the Gates are pasted behind the stove and on the door respectively. Lucky red mottoes are stuck on the door lintel. The family eat together, having worshipped the gods of Heaven and Earth, local and personal gods, and their ancestors. At midnight the family bow before the head of the household and the New Year is let in with fireworks and incense. All business ceases for at least a week and the festival officially finishes on the 15th of the month with the Festival of Lanterns when fireworks are once more set off and lanterns of all shapes and sizes decorate buildings.

Tsao Wang, the Kitchen God   (6 min.)

Tsao Wang, the Kitchen God, has his picture behind the stove in a Chinese house. Every day, three sweetly smelling joss sticks are burnt before the picture but otherwise very little notice is taken of him. Except at the very end of the old year. On the 24th day of the 12th month Tsao Wang is called up to Heaven by the August Supreme Emperor of Jade, Yu Huang Shang Ti, and commanded to make a report on everything the family has done throughout the year. Of course the family want the Ruler of Heaven to have a good report of their behaviour and so offerings of wine and sweets are made to the picture on this day. There is even some straw for the god's horse. Before the picture of Tsao Wang is solemnly burnt, to send him on his way to Heaven, his mouth is

23

smeared with honey so that he will only say sweet things to the Emperor of Jade about the family.

*

Tsao Wang was once a poor man, a mason by trade, who lived in China long ago. He was a good workman and very honest, but he lived amongst people who were selfish and dishonest and so he never made very much money.

If he did a job of stone cutting the work was always carefully and neatly done. Because of this it took him longer than the other stonemasons to do the work so he never seemed to earn enough.

Finally, Tsao Wang became so poor that he did not have enough money to feed his wife and himself. And, although they loved each other deeply, they came to a painful decision that would provide food enough for them both. Tsao Wang would sell his wife to another man.

And so it happened that sadly they were parted. Tsao Wang went back alone to his poor hut with enough money to keep him alive, while his wife went to the house of a rich merchant to be married.

Some time later, the rich merchant called Tsao Wang to do some stone work for him. He knew that Tsao Wang could be trusted to do an honest day's work. While Tsao Wang worked, his wife came and stood nearby, but she dared say nothing to him. Tsao Wang, however, did not now recognise her, dressed as she was as a rich man's wife, and he said nothing to her.

But the good wife wanted still to help the husband she loved. She ordered sesame cakes to be made in the kitchen and sent them to Tsao Wang as he worked. But before they were sent she slipped a gold coin into the middle of each one.

Gratefully Tsao Wang thanked the servant who brought the cakes to him and wrapped them up to take home.

On the way home Tsao Wang stopped at a tea house. As he sipped his tea he took out his cakes and offered one to another traveller who sat at his table. The other man bit into his cake and found himself with a mouthful of gold coin. Noticing that Tsao Wang had not yet eaten his cake he quickly offered to buy all the cakes from him for a very good price.

It seemed to Tsao Wang that his luck was in for the second time that day and thankfully he accepted the generous offer.

The next day Tsao Wang found out the truth from a servant at the rich merchant's house and he realised that all his good luck seemed to have gone bad. He had lived a life of honesty and had suffered poverty; he had loved his wife and had to sell her; and then he had not even recognised her and had actually sold the gift meant to help him. He felt that life was no longer worth living and went straight back home where, in despair, he killed himself.

But before Yen Wang Yeh, the First Lord of Hell, could snatch his soul away, the August Emperor of Jade caught him and raised him to Heaven, and for his goodness and honesty Tsao Wang was made into a god, the god with the duty to report on the behaviour of everybody, each New Year.

*

On New Year's Day Tsao Wang returns to the house. Offerings are made to him again and a new picture of him is put up behind the kitchen fire. The god is welcomed back with fireworks and great rejoicing. During the past few days he has not been there to see what the members of the family have been up to, but everyone is pleased to see him back, because the house has been without his protection. And so, although the family only take notice of Tsao Wang at New Year, Tsao Wang watches over them all the year through.

*

May Heaven guard you and keep you
In comfort and safety,
In health and strength,
Giving you every blessing,
Giving you good fortune
And giving you wealth.

May Heaven guard you and keep you,
Making your crops grow well,
And sending you nothing but good.
May Heaven send down a hundred favours
And so many blessings
That the day is not long enough for them all.

(from the Shih Ching, the Confucian Book of Odes, *c*.800 BCE)

The Dragon Boat Festival

(*5th of the fifth*)
June

Races are held in long, narrow, dragon-headed boats in commemoration of the suicide by drowning of the 3rd century BCE poet, Chu Yuan. His honest advice was spurned by his corrupt lord and his death was in protest. Triangular dumplings are eaten to commemorate the food thrown into the sea to stop the fishes eating the hero's body.

However, there is perhaps a more ancient connection with weather lore, the festival falling near to the summer solstice and the dragon being the bringer of rain. Four Dragon Kings, the Lung Wang, each ruling a sea at the cardinal points, live in crystal palaces beneath the waves. They take their orders directly from the Supreme August Emperor of Jade, Yu Huang Shang Ti, as to where and when to distribute rain. Despite their importance in the mythological hierarchy they receive scant attention from the people who treat the local dragon kings of their own wells and rivers and lakes with more deference. In times of drought or deluge processions are held where long dragon effigies are carried by a great train of people, supporting the body and tail.

Li Ching the Rainmaker   (10 min.)

Li Ching was a warrior from the city who liked to spend his holidays each year at a tiny village up in the mountains. Here he spent his time hunting. Each year he enjoyed his holiday with the simple people of the mountain village, and they in turn were pleased to see him.

Dusk was falling one evening when Li Ching suddenly spotted a magnificent deer up on the hillside. He had been about to return to the village but he could not resist chasing this beast. Here and there the deer darted, across the wooded hillside, up hills and through valleys – and then it was gone.

Li Ching realised with a fright that it was now very nearly dark and that he had followed the deer so far that he was well and truly lost.

As he sat on his horse, wondering what to do, he could see a light gleaming through the trees some distance away. Riding up, he saw a great house rising tall and proud in the midst of the wild forest. Li Ching knocked loudly at the door which was opened after some time by a servant.

The warrior explained his problem and begged for a night's shelter. But the servant was not very helpful. It seemed that the lords of the house were away and it would not be right for the lady of the house, their mother, to receive guests while they were not at home. However, the servant went off to ask.

The servant returned:

'Her Ladyship will take you in as you are lost and in need of help.'

Li Ching was led into the house, a very fine building for the middle of a forest! In the great hall Li Ching was received by the lady who stood with great dignity; she was well dressed and clearly a person of nobility.

'Welcome to our palace,' said the lady. 'I should not entertain a guest with the masters of the house, my sons, away, but as you obviously need help, I am pleased to offer it.'

Li Ching was fed a banquet and then taken to a luxurious bedchamber where he could spend the night. As he began to get ready for bed there came a tremendous hammering at the outside door.

'Orders from the Lord of Heaven,' shouted a voice. 'Rain is to be delivered by your eldest son, the Dragon King, over an area a thousand kilometres square. The rain is to be gentle but thorough and must stop at sunrise. Orders of the Lord of Heaven.'

Next, Li Ching heard the lady of the house talking with her servants.

'What shall I do? My sons are far far away and there is no time to call them back tonight. But the Lord of Heaven will punish us if his orders are not carried out.'

'What about our mortal guest?' suggested one of the servants. 'He's obviously a good horseman. Perhaps he could deliver the rain in the Dragon King's place.'

A servant was sent to fetch Li Ching.

'You must know now that you are a guest in a dragon palace,' said the lady. 'I have orders for my dragon sons to deliver rain over a certain area. Unfortunately they are far away on other business. Would you consent to undertake the task? If you can handle a good horse and can follow orders exactly you will find it an easy night's work.'

Li Ching said he was glad to help and the dragon lady was delighted.

Up into the night sky galloped the horse. Whenever it stopped and whinnied Li Ching had to dip his finger into a very tiny pot and let one drop drip on to the horse's mane. The horse would then shake his head and rain would pour down on the lands below.

And so the night passed and Li Ching delivered rain in place of the Dragon King wherever the horse showed him. Morning was drawing near and his job was nearly finished when Li Ching found himself looking down on the village in the mountains where he had been staying.

'The people there have been so kind to me over the years and now is my chance to help them. There has been no rain there for some time now; the wells are dry and the crops are looking parched. I shall give them an extra drop of rain.'

Li Ching dipped his finger into the little pot and shook it hard on to the horse's mane so that a whole shower of drops fell. The horse shook his head and then made for home.

When they returned to the palace in the forest Li Ching found the noble lady in tears. The few extra drops that Li Ching had given his favourite village had caused a torrential downpour on earth. The whole valley was flooded, the village was completely under water, houses and crops ruined, and surely no-one could be left alive.

And already the messengers had come from the Lord of Heaven and punished the Dragon Queen with eighty lashes of the whip. Punishment lay in store for her sons when they returned.

'I don't blame you at all, Li Ching. I should never have given the task to you. But go quickly before my dragon sons return. I fear their anger.'

So saying the lady of the house handed Li Ching a bag full of large and precious pearls.

The warrior found his way back to the valley where the village had been. One or two rooftops showed above the rising waters and Li Ching feared the worst. But to his delight on some high ground a little way off he saw the villagers huddled together, wet and cold and frightened but alive. Li Ching had been slow with his pot of water and the people had heard the thunder approach and escaped to safety.

And so Li Ching had a second chance to help his friends. He handed over the bag of pearls and with the money the people were able to build a fine new village after the flood waters had gone down.

In later years Li Ching became a famous general and the Duke of Wei. He had more success in battle than he ever had as a rainmaker!

*

Rain is of the greatest importance to people whose lives are bound up with the round of the farming year. Here is a prayer to the god who invented farming, Hou Chi, Lord Millet:

Mighty is Hou Chi,
Partner of the Lord of Heaven.
Thanks to you
All we thronging people are fed.
You gave us wheat and barley
As God commanded
Not just here and there
But near, far and for ever
Throughout the lands of China.

(from the Shih Ching, the Confucian Book of Odes, c.800 BCE)

The Birthday of Confucius

October

At the pre-dawn ceremony schoolboys in ancient costume perform dances dating from the Tang dynasty (618–907 CE) while traditionally dressed officials solemnly carry out the religious functions in commemoration of the sage. Confucius is especially revered by educators, and schoolchildren are required to attend the ceremony, although many other people do so too. After the solemnities a boar is roasted and everyone competes to pull out a bristle.

Kung Fu Tzu, Master Kung (latinised to Confucius) was born in the tiny village of Tsou in Shantung province some 500 km south of Peking. He was a tall ugly man, self-taught, and with very high ideals as to how government should be run. He was never able to achieve high office nor could he persuade any prince to try out his philosophy of politics. He lived for many years in exile, teaching and studying, and died, disappointed, and an apparent failure in 479 BCE. However, his practical philosophy of personal virtue, of self-improvement through learning and knowledge, and of service to others has had an incalculable influence on Chinese behaviour and thought since his time.

Confucius   (6 min.)

Confucius lived well over 2,000 years ago in China and is believed by his followers to be the wisest man the world has ever known.

When Confucius was only three, his father had died leaving his mother with very little money. Confucius had to learn to look after himself and his family while he was still very young. When he grew up he said:

'When I was young we were very poor. That's probably why I can do so many different odd jobs now.'

Although the family was poor Confucius managed to learn to read and write. He taught himself enough to get a job adding up the accounts of the most important family in the state. Confucius always taught how important it was to be educated. Without learning a man is nothing; with learning and knowledge a man becomes understanding, good and kind. Confucius said:

'Without learning the wise become foolish; by learning the foolish become wise.'

*

When he was young Confucius did not mix easily with other people. He was shy and embarrassed because of his looks. He stood over two metres tall and was clumsy and awkward and ugly; his eyes were wide and staring, his nose was crooked and his teeth were goofy. But, although his mind was brilliant and his heart was gentle, he was the type of person that others like to make fun of and joke about. So Confucius spent his time hidden away, reading in the city libraries, or listening and talking to the Duke's blind musicians. He discussed anything and everything with the Duke's writers and historians and priests and artists – people who cared nothing about his looks but admired his intelligence and interest.

And so, through his own hard work, Confucius became more and more learned.

One day this clumsy, awkward youth decided that he ought to learn to play a musical instrument. He went to the Music Master of the city and asked to be taught to play the zither. The Master looked at the tall boy with his thick fingers who seemed to find it difficult to even walk straight – but he said 'yes'.

For over a week Confucius tried hard to do what the Master of Music told him. For over a week the Master gritted his teeth and covered his ears as Confucius banged away. But at last he had heard enough.

'I think you've had enough practice on the zither. Shall we try something else now?'

'Oh no,' Confucius replied. 'I've got the hang of the tune now. It's just the rhythm I can't get.'

So the Master let him practise some more. After Confucius had plucked away at the strings for several more days, the Master of Music said:

'I think you've had enough practice with the rhythm now. Shall we go on to something else?'

'Oh no,' answered Confucius, 'I'm trying to capture the mood of the music now. Let me practise a little longer.'

And again the Master put up with the noise.

'You've surely caught the mood of the music. Do you think we could move on to something different now?'

'I have practised playing the zither and mastered the tune, the rhythm and the mood of this piece of music,' said Confucius, 'but I haven't yet understood the man who wrote the music.'

The Master of Music allowed Confucius to continue his practice and began to realise now that there was more to this ugly awkward youth than first met the eye. Confucius was not happy just to learn to play the zither, which was difficult enough, he did not want just to understand and feel the music, he wanted to get to know the soul of the composer of the music.

The Master was watching with admiration as Confucius began to draw the music from the instrument, when the boy suddenly stopped playing, smiles all over his big face.

'I know who wrote this piece of music,' he said. 'He was a tall man, a great man. He had keen eyes and a mind like the Emperor of Heaven. It was the great King Wen, of ancient times, who wrote this music.'

The Master stood up in amazement and bowed low before his young pupil.

'You are right,' said the Master of Music. 'King Wen did write the music you played.'

*

Confucius believed that anybody could become a good person through determination and by thoughtful education, and the study of all sorts of things. Confucius said:

'The best man is careful of these things:

his eyes, so that he may observe;

his ears, that he may learn;

his face, that it may always reflect kindness;

his manners, that they might show respect for other people;

his words that they may be true;

his dealings with other people, that they may be fair.'

(from the Lun Yu, the Analects or Collected Sayings, c.350 BCE)

When he was asked by one of his followers to sum up all his ideas, Confucius said all his teaching could be put into one word: 'reciprocity'.

He was asked what he meant by this and he replied:

'Do not do to other people what you would not want them to do to you.'

Christian Festivals

Epiphany

6 January

Epiphany (Greek: the showing) celebrates the manifestation of Jesus to the Gentiles, the non-Jews, represented by the Magi, the three wise men or astrologers. They are traditionally named Melchior, Caspar and Balthazar, one white, one black and one yellow-skinned, symbolising all the world's races. They came from the east following a star (possibly a conjunction of the planets Jupiter and Saturn, the former supposedly lucky, the latter the protector of Israel) bringing gifts of gold (symbolising kingship), frankincense, a fragrantly burning tree gum (symbolic of holiness) and myrrh, an embalming ointment (a symbol of suffering and death).

The murder of all the boys in Bethlehem under two years of age was ordered by King Herod in an attempt to kill the child destined to be 'the King of the Jews'. The slaughter is commemorated on Holy Innocents' Day, 28 December.

This festival is the last of the twelve days of the traditional Christmas holiday (q.v.) and in the United Kingdom on Twelfth Night, the eve of Epiphany, decorations are removed, the illuminated fir-tree is taken from the house, and greetings cards are taken down from display.

There are a number of different legends about the three kings with themes similar to the story from Russia included here.

In Eastern Orthodox tradition this festival celebrates not the adoration of the Magi but the baptism of Jesus in the River Jordan (see Shrove Tuesday) in commemoration of which people carry out ceremonies of blessing the waters – the sea, lakes and rivers. For Orthodox Christians the manifestation of Jesus is the beginning of his ministry to the world which began after his baptism. The three wise men are remembered on Christmas Day.

The Three Wise Men   (4 min.)

Melchior, Caspar, and Balthazar, one white, one black, one yellow-skinned, had travelled from Persia over high cold mountains, and through dry hot deserts following the bright star which moved always westward.

They arrived at last at the palace of King Herod, a strong ruler but a cruel man. They thought that the royal palace would be the place where a saviour of the people and king of the Jews would be born. And in the great palace in Jerusalem the three wise men knelt before Herod:

'Where is the child who is born to be king of the Jews? We have followed his star and we want to bow down before him.'

Herod was worried when he heard this. He knew that the men were not fools – he had to take them seriously. So what did they mean by talking of the 'King of the Jews'? Herod was king and no child had been born to him for a long time. Herod called his own wise men and advisers together and asked them what this meant. They told him that the Old Testament of the Bible prophesies the birth of a saviour of the Jews in the town of Bethlehem, a few miles from Jerusalem.

Herod called the wise men to him in private:

'I want you to go on to Bethlehem to worship the new king. When you have found him, be sure to come back and tell me where he is so that I too can bow down before him.'

The wise men couldn't know that Herod meant to kill the child – he would have no rival kings in his country – so the three set out to the small town of Bethlehem still following the star.

They soon found the baby with his parents Mary and Joseph. They weren't rich or famous; they were poor, ordinary people. But the wise men seemed to know that they had found the child they were looking for, and they knelt before him, leaving him their gifts of gold, frankincense, and myrrh.

That night the wise men dreamed that they should not go back to see Herod. The next morning they set out for their own country by a different route.

Joseph also had a dream – he dreamed that an angel came to him warning him of King Herod's anger. The angel told him to take Jesus and Mary away to Egypt for there was evil in Herod's mind. The next day Joseph and his family set off.

It was some time before Herod realised that he had been tricked by the three wise men and that they weren't going to come back to report to him. And his anger was great indeed. He ordered that every boy under the age of two years should be killed by his soldiers. Immediately the order went out. The soldiers marched to Bethlehem and killed every baby boy in the town and the nearby villages. Herod was sure now that there would be no other king of the Jews but him.

It was not many months before Joseph had another dream in which an angel told him that King Herod had died and that it would be safe to go home again. Herod's son was now king, so Joseph took his family back a safe way and returned to the tiny village of Nazareth where he had been a carpenter. So, although he was born in Bethlehem, Jesus is often called by the name of Jesus of Nazareth.

Baboushka   (4 min.)

Many years ago in Russia lived an old woman called Baboushka. She was poor but she always had something to give to children, for she loved children.

One cold winter's night there came to the door of her small cottage three very richly-dressed men: one white, one black, and the third yellow-skinned. They asked if they could rest at Baboushka's cottage.

'I've nothing to offer you,' said Baboushka, 'for I am very poor. But what I have is yours and you're very welcome to stay here if you like.'

The three men came in and rested and warmed themselves around Baboushka's tiny fire. And as they sat they talked together of the journey they were making. It seemed that they had come all the way from Persia following a very bright star. (Baboushka had noticed an especially bright star in the western sky). They were going to find a baby, who was to be born in Bethlehem in Judaea. They spoke of the baby as being the Prince of Peace and the one who would save the world.

'Can I give you a present for the baby?' asked the old lady. 'I do like children.'

'Better than that,' said one of the men. 'You can come with us to see the child yourself.'

'Oh, thank you,' answered Baboushka. 'I will.'

But then Baboushka thought again. The night was dark and very cold and Bethlehem sounded as if it was a long, long way away. She was an old woman, after all, and she had her house to look after. She was silent for some time and then she said:

'It's very kind of you to offer to take me with you, but I think I'd better not come.'

When the three men were warmed and rested they decided that the time had come for them to carry on with their journey. They put on their heavy cloaks and wrapped themselves up before facing the cold Russian night. As they left the cottage, one of them said: 'Are you sure you won't come with us, Baboushka?'

But Baboushka shook her head sadly. She wanted to see the baby but didn't think she could make the journey. And off the wise men went.

Next morning Baboushka thought about what the three men had said. And the more she thought, the more she wished she'd gone with them. She didn't know anything about princes, but she knew what babies liked and she was sure she could find some presents to please a small child. She made up her mind. She would go. She'd set off right away and catch up with the three wise men. Baboushka searched out a basketful of toys, wrapped herself up warmly, and set off to follow the wise men.

She went down to the village and asked some people there if they'd seen three wise men travelling that way.

'Oh, yes, Baboushka,' they replied. 'They went further on towards the West.'

Baboushka left some gifts for the children of the village and went on.

She asked again at the next village.

'Oh, yes,' answered the people. 'They went further on towards the West.'

And so Baboushka left some presents for the children there and went on.

Each village she came to Baboushka was told that the wise men had passed but that they had gone further on. Baboushka always remembered to leave something for the children before she followed them.

Baboushka is still travelling on. And when Christmas-time approaches Christian children in Russia hope that she will leave something for them before she travels yet further on.

*

The Gloria

Glory be to God on high
And on earth peace to friends of God.
We praise you.
We bless you.
We adore you.
We glorify you.
We give thanks for your great glory.

(from the Roman Catholic Mass)

St. Valentine's Day

14 February

This secular festival is celebrated by the sending of unsigned romantic cards to loved ones. The date is supposedly that when birds choose their mates and takes only its name from the Christian bishop, Valentine, who was executed in the reign of the Roman emperor, Claudius II Gothicus (born 214 CE, ruled 268–270).

St. Valentine   (3 min.)

There came to the throne of the Roman Empire a soldier called Claudius. During his time there was constant trouble from countries in the east where a fierce tribe called the Goths were forever attacking Roman towns and forts. The trouble was that the Goths were often successful and would burn the town, kill the people, and steal anything they could find. Claudius was getting more and more worried. He was the ruler of the greatest empire the world had ever seen and yet a horde of savage uncivilised tribesmen could beat the famous Roman army. Claudius decided that his troops were getting soft and he figured that the reason must be that they were all too happy at home with their wives and families. The soldiers had lost their will to fight.

Orders went out from Emperor Claudius that from that date onwards no Roman soldier would be allowed to marry.

Of course they were many who still wanted to get married and there were priests, especially Christian priests, who would marry them in secret. One of these priests was called Valentine. Valentine was the Bishop of Terni, a city dangerously close to the palace of the Emperor in Rome.

It was not long before the secret marriages were discovered. Valentine was arrested and thrown into prison. The cell was small and dark and damp and the food was bad. But Valentine was lucky: the jailer in charge of his prison had a daughter and she often took it upon herself to care for the prisoners. She did her best to make things better for the Bishop by bringing him dry straw to sleep on and by giving him more than his ration of food.

At last orders came that Valentine was to be put to death. He was led out of prison, beaten with clubs, and then beheaded. When the jailer's daughter was clearing out the cell afterwards, she found a little note of thanks from the Bishop. On the bottom he had signed it: 'Your Valentine'.

Shrove Tuesday or Pancake Tuesday

February/early March

Commemorating the forty days contemplating his mission spent by Jesus in the desert, the Lenten fast begins on Ash Wednesday, the day following Shrove Tuesday. On this day western Christians (especially Roman Catholics) confess their sins and are absolved or shriven, hence the name of the day. Lent is a period of abstinence, so joyous festivities used to be held as a preparation, including the eating of foods forbidden during the next forty days. Pancakes were made to use up surplus eggs, butter and milk; mixed with flour to a batter, they are fried lightly in a pan, tossed in the air, and fried on the other side. Traditionally they are eaten with sugar, lemon juice or jam. In some Catholic countries and in the Caribbean, Shrove Tuesday celebrations are great public occasions with processions and carnivals in the streets.

The Baptism of Jesus   (5 min.)

Jesus's cousin, John, lived the life of a hermit in the desert, eating locusts, and honey from wild bees' nests, and wearing rough camel-hair clothes. He would stand by the River Jordan at a crossing-place where Jews and Romans and travellers of all kinds forded the river. He was tall, strong, rough and loud, and he wasn't the least bit afraid of telling everyone, whether poor or important, exactly what he thought of them:

'You're all wicked sinners,' he shouted at the travellers. 'Repent your sins. Tell God you're sorry before he punishes you. Don't think God will do you any favours just because you're Jews and think that you're his favourite chosen people. God expects more of you. Repent your sins. Come and be baptised.'

Many people listened to John. They waded into the river and he washed them in the waters as a sign that their souls were clean and that they would try to lead a better life in future.

Some wealthy people came to be baptised:

'How can we lead better lives?' they asked.

'If you have two shirts, give one to the poor. If you have more food than you need, give some away.'

Some tax-gatherers were among those being baptised:

'How can we show we are sorry?' they asked.

'Stop cheating people out of their money,' answered John.

There were also soldiers by the river:
'How should we live?'
'You have enough pay to live on; don't bully the ordinary people to give
you more.'

*

The people called this man John the Baptist. Many wondered if he was the
man the Bible said would be the saviour of the Jews. They came from miles
around to hear him speak and to wash away their sins in the River Jordan.
John always said the same thing when they asked him if he was the saviour of
the Jews:
'There is one who will come from among you, far mightier than I. I am not
even good enough to fasten his shoes. I baptise you with water; he will baptise
with the Holy Spirit of God.'
One day a queue of people were waiting to be baptised, when John
recognised his cousin from Nazareth, Jesus.
'I can't baptise you,' said John. 'It is you should baptise me.'
But Jesus insisted and so John baptised him. As Jesus stood in the water, it
seemed to John that the skies opened and he saw the Holy Spirit of God come
down in the shape of a dove and rest upon Jesus's head. John heard the voice
of God saying:
'This is my son, my Beloved, on whom my favour rests.'
John said to the crowds:
'This is the one I said would come from among you. This is the Lamb of
God who will take away the sins of the world.'
People still gathered round John after Jesus's baptism, for Jesus had no
followers yet and had gone into the desert to think over the task that faced
him. John was attracting so many people to him that the priests and the King
began to think of him as a trouble-maker. Spies were sent to listen to him and
when he was heard proclaiming how wicked the King was, he was arrested,
taken to Jerusalem and thrown into prison. Although John knew that death
could not be far away, he was happy because he knew that his work was over.
He had prepared the way for the message of Jesus. Now Jesus was to start
preaching to the people himself.

*

Many Christian church services use the words of the Bible as an important
part of their worship. These words are taken from the Eastern Orthodox
Church:
O Lord God, heavenly King, God the Father Almighty;
O Lord, the only-begotten Son, Jesus Christ;

And you, O Holy Spirit,
O Lord God, Lamb of God, Son of the Father, that take away the sins of
    the world, have mercy on us.
You that take away the sins of the world,
Accept our prayer.
You that sit on the right hand of the Father, have mercy upon us.
For only you are holy, you only are the Lord, O Jesus Christ,
To the glory of God the Father. Amen.

(from the great Doxology of the Eastern Orthodox Church)

Ash Wednesday

February/early March

*Ash Wednesday, the first day of Lent, is so named because in some churches
ashes, the symbol of repentance, are marked in the sign of a cross on the
foreheads of the congregation. Sometimes the previous year's Palm Sunday
(q.v.) palms are burned and used for the purpose. Lent (from the Old English
word meaning spring) is the period of abstinence and fasting commemorating the
forty days that Jesus spent in the wilderness in meditation. Here he was tempted
three times by the Devil but resisted, and emerged to choose his disciples and
begin his earthly mission. Lent ends on the eve of Easter day (q.v.).*

Jesus is Tempted by the Devil   (3 min.)

After Jesus had been baptised by John the Baptist he set out into the wild and
lonely wilderness. All the prophets before him had spent time in the desert to
give themselves chance to think, away from the hubbub of the towns. John
himself had spent years in the desert – now it was Jesus's turn.

    He left the roads and went into a harsh dry land of burning sun and heat,
where no men lived and few plants or animals could survive. He climbed the
rocky mountains and sat in thought trying to decide what God wanted him to
do. As the searing heat of the day was followed by the agonising cold of the
night Jesus became weak and hungry. As he thought, there came to him the
voice of the Devil:

    'If you are the Son of God, tell these stones to become bread.'

Jesus was famished but called out with all his strength:

'Man cannot live by bread alone; man needs to live by the word of God.'

Jesus was led by the Devil to a place high up on the Great Temple in Jerusalem:

'If you are the Son of God, throw yourself down. After all the Bible says that God will save you.'

Jesus answered the Devil:

'The Bible also says that you must not try to test God.'

Jesus found himself on a very high mountain from where he could see all the countries of the world:

'I will give you all this if you will only bow down and worship me,' said the Devil.

'The Bible says that you should bow down and worship only God. Now get away from me, Satan.'

After he had overcome his temptations and spent forty days and forty nights in the desert, Jesus set out for the towns again. He knew now what the task was that God had given him.

*

I stretch out my hands to you, O God, who forgives the sins of the guilty, and beg you to forgive me even though I do not deserve it.

I beg you to keep my mind safe from the tricks of the Devil, to keep my eyes safe from the temptations of the wicked, to keep my ears safe from selfish or foolish talk, and to keep my hands that they may always serve you and that I may always try to give you glory. (from the Syrian Orthodox Church Liturgy, 4th century CE)

St. David's Day

1st March

St. David, the patron saint of Wales, lived some time during the 6th century in Wales. He became a priest and travelled widely, including visits to England and a pilgrimage to Jerusalem. On his return he founded a number of monasteries in Wales including one in the valley of Glyn Rhosyn, now St. David's, Dyfed. He became archbishop of Wales and was held in great honour by the Celtic church. He is reputed to have died at a great age on 1st March and is depicted with his emblem the dove or the leek.

St. David, Patron Saint of Wales   (4 min.)

David was a priest who lived in Wales. He was a small man but a very strong speaker. People would come for miles over the mountains to hear him preach. While he was on his travels around the country, and sometimes when he went to England, David would hear people talking about Jesus. Some of them would say: 'If Jesus was the Son of God, then he couldn't have been a man like us. He must have been a spirit or a ghost.'

Throughout Wales there was talk and argument about this: some people said that Jesus was a spirit; others said that he was a real living man. Eventually the argument became so fierce that the leaders of the Welsh church called the priests and bishops together to discuss the problem. David was one of those chosen to go.

The great meeting was attended by so many people that it had to be held outside. When it came to David's turn, although he was small and couldn't be seen properly, he spoke so powerfully and well that everyone was silent and listened carefully. David said that Jesus *was* God, but it was important to remember as well that he *was* an ordinary person just like you and me.

The legend says that while David was speaking, the ground under him seemed to rise up and by the time he had finished, he seemed to be standing on a hill above the heads of the other people there. It is said that a white dove came and landed on his shoulder – the white dove is a sign of the Holy Spirit of God, and people believed this showed that David was speaking the word of God.

After the meeting most people now agreed with David, and everyone was so impressed by his speech that they decided to make him the head of the Welsh church, the Archbishop of Wales.

David still lived in the monastery he had started up at Glyn Rhosyn, even though he was the Archbishop. Life was very hard there and the monks had to do all the work themselves – grow their own food, cook, clean, and tidy up. When they weren't working they were praying. And David lived in exactly the same way as the other monks.

Although they worked hard and didn't eat more than they really needed, the monastery was always open for travellers and for the poor. They always got a welcome, a good meal, and a warm and comfortable bed for the night. The monks themselves slept on hard wooden beds and ate mainly leeks which grew well on the mountain soil.

David lived to be very old. When he died the Welsh people remembered him so kindly that they made him their own patron saint..

*

The Welsh people are famous for their singing and St. David's Day is one of the times they get together to sing in Welsh. The Welsh national plant is the leek that St. David's monks used to eat, and on St. David's Day there are competitions to see who can eat the most raw leeks! – they have a mild oniony taste. At one time some people thought that the leek wasn't dignified enough for a national plant, and they chose the daffodil instead. It is said that wild daffodils begin to open on 1st March.

*

One of the most famous Welsh hymns is called 'Arglwydd, arwain tryw'r anialwch' – 'Guide me, O Thou great Jehovah'.

Guide me, O Thou great Jehovah,
Pilgrim through this barren land;
I am weak, but Thou art mighty;
Hold me with Thy powerful hand:
Bread of heaven!
Feed me now and evermore.

(by William Williams 1717–1791 CE;
translation by Peter Williams 1722–1796
from the Methodist Hymn Book)

St. Patrick's Day

17 March

Patrick was born in 373 CE, of wealthy parents, in the Marches of Wales near the River Severn (though some sources say it was in Scotland). Captured by a warring band and sold as a slave to an Irish chief (a common practice at that time), he later escaped via Killala (Cill Ala), County Mayo, to France where he entered the monastery at Tours (Indre-et-Loire) and trained to become a priest. He returned to Britain but later left for Rome where he became a bishop. He had always felt a need to take Christianity to Ireland and left with a band of missionaries in 432 CE. He preached at the Hill of Tara, County Meath, the seat of the high kings of Ireland from prehistoric times until the 6th century CE, and spent the next 30 years of his life converting the Irish until his death in 461 CE. He is buried at Downpatrick, County Down.

Since the Middle Ages, Croagh Patrick, County Mayo (The Rick of Saint Patrick, 765 m high) has been a place of pilgrimage. In the Lent of 441 St.

Patrick spent the 40 days and nights there in fast and prayer. The Pattern (i.e. prilgrimage) is held on the last Sunday in July.

(The Celtic feast of Beltane that is mentioned, was celebrated on 1st May and was a spring festival associated with fertility during which all domestic fires were put out to be relit from one public sacrificial fire. Cattle were driven between Beltane fires for protection from disease whilst the people danced sunwise around them.)

St. Patrick, Patron Saint of Ireland   (7 min.)

Patrick was a boy who lived in a very rich house in Wales. He never had to work and never would have to, because his parents owned many slaves. Patrick led a happy and peaceful life – until he was 16.

There had been some trouble lately in the lands near Patrick's home. The argument had broken out into fighting and some local villages had been raided and burned. When Patrick was walking in the fields one day a band of soldiers galloping by grabbed him and dragged him off. Though he struggled and shouted, there was no-one to hear and he could not get free. He was taken to a seaport where he was pushed about and treated roughly, and where a sea captain bought Patrick for sale abroad as a slave.

The ship set sail across a stormy sea and Patrick left his father and mother and his home further and further behind. He had been brought up as a Christian and, as the ship pitched up and down on the waves, Patrick tried to remember the prayers he had learned at home. But it was difficult to pray as he was both sea-sick and sick with fear as to what was going to happen to him.

Patrick was taken to Ireland and there he was sold to a chief as a slave. His job was that of a shepherd. He was not treated cruelly, but a life as a shepherd boy in a foreign land was much harder than the life he had led, and he often dreamed of home. As the years went by Patrick grew to love the Irish people, but he was still a Christian and always wished he could turn them away from their belief in many gods and their belief in magic.

After a long time planning and preparing, Patrick made his escape. He had gathered some food for the journey and when he was left alone with the sheep, he sneaked off to return to Britain. He found a ship which took him to France and it was not until many years later that he reached his own home again.

Patrick became a priest and went to Rome where he was made a bishop. But he always remembered the Irish and swore that one day he would go back to Ireland. At last, at the age of 60, he set sail and landed in Ireland just before the great spring festival of Beltane.

At Beltane everyone had to put out their fires and wait for the High King of

Ireland to light his. When this was done torches were lit at the King's fire and carried all over the land to light the fires again. Feasts and dancing took place to welcome in the spring.

Now Patrick knew that if he wanted to persuade the Irish people to become Christians he would have to persuade the High King first. But he also knew that he had no chance of ever getting to see the King. He decided he had to do something spectacular.

On Beltane night when all the fires had been put out, when all the villages were in darkness and the High King stood ready to light the sacred fire, suddenly on another hill some distance away a torch burst into flame and a fire began to burn.

'Who dares to burn a fire at Beltane?' shouted the King. 'Guards, fetch him here.'

A man was soon brought in chains before him. He wore strange clothes and a cross around his neck and he was very calm as he stood before the King. The clothes were those of a Christian bishop. The man was Patrick. Of course Patrick was nervous, but he had come to preach the word of God and so he knew he had to show no fear. The King and court were all shocked that anyone had dared to light a fire on Beltane night, but they were all impressed by the old man who stood so proudly before them. And when Patrick began to tell first the long story of his life, and then the story of Jesus Christ, all listened in silence.

When Patrick had finished, the King was quiet for a long time. He had been deeply interested in Patrick's story, even though Patrick had told him that his beliefs were all wrong. He ordered Patrick to be locked up for the night and the feast began. The King would deal with the prisoner in the morning.

The King saw Patrick the next day and for many days after that. He grew to like Patrick and began to understand what he was preaching, until at last he decided that he would become a Christian. Patrick was delighted and asked the King for his permission to go around Ireland to convert the people. For the next 30 years Patrick travelled around Ireland preaching and teaching, founding churches and monasteries, and converting the people to Christianity.

*

There was one thing that the High King had found hard to understand and many of the people did too. This is the Christian idea that, although there is only one God, He is thought of as three persons. God who created the world is called God the Father; when He lived as a man He was Jesus Christ, the Son; when He fills the hearts of men with His love He is called God the Holy Spirit. Christians say he is Three in One. Patrick explained this by picking the leaf of a little plant like clover that grows all over Ireland, called the shamrock. The shamrock has one leaf that is split into three parts. Patrick told the Irish that there are three parts to the leaf but there is only one leaf. He said God is like that. The Irish people remembered the shamrock and still wear it as their national emblem, especially on St. Patrick's Day.

*

A breastplate is the part of a knight's armour that protects his chest and his heart. St. Patrick called this prayer his breastplate:

St. Patrick's Breastplate

May the strength of God steer us,
May the power of God keep us,
May the wisdom of God teach us,
May the hand of God protect us,
May the way of God lead us,
May the shield of God defend us,
May the angels of God guard us.

The Annunciation of the Blessed Virgin Mary (Lady Day)

25 March

Held nine months before Christmas Day (q.v.), this feast celebrates the announcing to Mary that she was to conceive the Son of God through the Holy Spirit, the third person of the Christian Trinity of God. The Archangel Gabriel had told the old priest Zechariah in Jerusalem that his previously barren wife Elizabeth would bear a son, John, later 'the Baptist', the precurser of Jesus, and last of the prophets who prepared the Jews for the coming of their Messiah (literally 'the anointed one'). Six months later Gabriel told Elizabeth's cousin Mary that she would bear a son to be named Jesus. He gave proof that God's promises are kept, citing the case of Elizabeth. Christians see this as a fulfilment of the prophesies of the Old Testament (especially the Book of Isaiah) which makes reference to the virgin birth of Immanuel (literally 'God with us'), the deliverer of the Jews.

By the fourteenth century the English Church began its year on Lady Day rather than on Christmas Day. In 1752 the beginning of the civil and legal year was transferred from Lady Day to 1 January, but the financial year still retains the connection, although the year is now rounded off to begin on 1 April. In 1752 the Julian calendar was replaced by the Gregorian and 1752 lost eleven days. To avoid upsetting certain contracts renewable on Lady Day, 6 April (when the day would have been had the calendar not been altered) was styled Old Lady Day and this date is still held as the start of the Income Tax Year.

*

The Angel Gabriel Visits Mary   (3 min.)

Mary was a poor girl living in the village of Nazareth about two thousand years ago. Nothing ever happened in Nazareth – it was only a small place a long way from big exciting cities like Jerusalem. Nothing exciting ever happened to Mary.

One day while Mary was working in her mother's house, sweeping and cleaning, she felt that something or someone was in the room with her. As she turned she became aware of the presence of an angel. Of course Mary was shocked and afraid, but the Angel Gabriel spoke kindly to her:

'Do not be afraid, Mary, for God has been gracious to you.'

Gabriel went on to tell her that she was going to have a son, that she should call him Jesus and that her child would be king over Israel for ever.

Mary asked Gabriel:

'How can I be having a son when I've not even got a husband?'

'The Holy Spirit of God will come upon you,' answered Gabriel. 'Your son will be the Son of God.'

Gabriel told Mary that her cousin Elizabeth was also pregnant and would give birth to a son in just three months' time. Elizabeth was the wife of one of the priests of the great Temple in the city of Jerusalem. They were both quite old now and nobody had thought that they would ever have children.

'I am the Lord's servant,' said Mary, and the angel left her.

Soon after, Mary travelled to see her cousin in Jerusalem. It was true. Elizabeth was pregnant. Her husband had also had a vision of the Angel Gabriel. Zechariah had not believed the angel and had been struck dumb for doubting the word of God. Mary stayed with Elizabeth and Zechariah in Jerusalem until the baby was due to be born.

Elizabeth's baby was named John. Zechariah was able to speak again and told everyone that his son would grow up to be a prophet, and a teacher to the people of Israel. He would be a great man, but he would only prepare the way for the greatest of all.

*

These words are said by Christians on many occasions, as they are in the church service on this day:

Hail Mary, full of grace: the Lord is with you: blessed are you among women, and blessed is Jesus your son. (from the Roman Catholic Liturgy)

St. George's Day

23 April

George was born in the 3rd century CE *in the Roman province of Cappadocia (now eastern Turkey) and, after his father's Christian martyrdom, was taken by his mother to Lydda in Palestine (now Lod, Israel), a town about 40 km from Jerusalem. As a Roman officer he was expected to carry out Emperor Diocletian's persecution of the Christians whose refusal to acknowledge the Roman gods represented a threat to imperial authority; but George is said to have torn up the edict commanding all Christians to sacrifice to the Roman gods. After suffering numerous tortures, being beaten with staves and branded with irons, and still refusing to worship the Roman gods, George was put to death: in one story he was beheaded, in another, sawn in two. He died in the year of Diocletian's edict, 303* CE.

The knightly legends of St. George date from the 12th century Crusades when he was seen scaling the walls of Jerusalem and leading the charge at Antioch. Richard the Lionheart of England put his troops under the saint's protection; Edward III flew the cross of St. George from his ships and put the Order of the Garter in his care; Richard II ordered his troops to wear the red cross of the saint on their uniforms. It is from this time that the written legend of St. George and the dragon dates.

St. George and the Dragon   (4 min.)

Many hundreds of years ago there was a certain city, ruled over by a king and his queen. Their only child was a beautiful princess. It was a peaceful happy city until the day that a huge dragon arrived in a cloud of smoke and fire and began to burn the fields and farms. The terrified people ran and hid – they could do nothing against such a monster. For days the dragon did just as it liked until the countryside around the city was in ruins.

'We can't let this go on,' said the people. 'The dragon will be attacking the city next. But what can we do?'

'We'll have to negotiate with the dragon,' said one man, 'and see if we can do a deal with him.'

The King chose the bravest men in the city and they set out to meet the dragon. Everyone wondered if they'd ever come back. But they did – and they *had* made a deal with the dragon. But what a deal! The dragon said he would leave them alone, if, every day, they would send him a child for his dinner.

'We can't agree to do that,' said some of the people.

'I don't see that we can do anything else,' said the King.

The names of all the children of the city were written on pieces of paper and put in a barrel. The King had to take the first one out. He unfolded the paper and on it was the name of his only daughter, the princess. Some people wanted to let the King choose another piece of paper but he refused.

'There can't be one law for the people and a different law for me,' he said. 'My daughter has been chosen, and she must go.'

Although she was terrified, the little princess said goodbye to her parents, and walked out of the city gates to meet the dragon. The people watched in silence and waited for the mighty roar that would tell them that the dragon had seen his dinner.

At that moment there rode into the city a knight on a fine white horse. He carried a white shield, marked with a red cross, and a lance. The people told him what had happened and begged him to help. Saying nothing, George spurred his horse and, with a great clattering of hooves, he charged out of the city gates.

He had not galloped far along the road when he saw the princess crying. Towering above her, spitting fire, belching smoke, and with a look of evil in its eyes, was an enormous green scaly dragon. It hissed hatred when it saw St. George. Then, with a roar like a volcano, beating its leathery wings, it rose into the air ready to fall on George; but the knight was too quick. As the monster came down, St. George thrust his lance up and speared its neck. With a scream of pain it fell dying to the earth. And, as the King and Queen and the cheering people rushed out to thank him, St. George drew his sword and struck off the monster's wicked head.

Saints are people who have given themselves completely to God; ordinary people find this more difficult to do. On the first Sunday of the New Year Methodist Christians hold a service to promise themselves to God. Here is part of the promise they make:

I am no longer my own, but yours.
Do what you want with me,
    put me among whatever people you want;
Put me to work, or put me to suffering;
Let me do a job for you,
    or be cast aside for you;
Let me be raised high for you,
    or brought down low for you;
Let me be full, let me be empty;
Let me have all things, let me have nothing;
Freely and with all my heart
I give up everything to you.

And now, O glorious and blessed God,
Father, Son and Holy Spirit,
You are mine, and I am yours.
So be it.
And the promise which I have made on earth,
Let it be heard in heaven.
Amen

(from the Service of Renewal of the Covenant with God
from the Methodist Book of Offices)

Palm Sunday

March/April

Palm Sunday falls one week before Easter Sunday and commemorates the triumphal palm-strewn entry of Jesus into Jerusalem. He rode a donkey into the city; traditionally the donkey took the clearly marked cross on its shoulders from this event – Jesus was put to death by being nailed to a cross. He knew that he was riding to his death at the hands of his enemies and this is borne in mind by Christians celebrating the day. Some churches are decorated with palm or willow branches, and crosses made of palm leaves or twigs are given to the congregation.

Jesus's Entry into Jerusalem   (4 min.)

Jesus was walking towards Jerusalem. He was famous throughout the land, but there were many who didn't like him. The King, the chief priests, the Romans all considered him to be a trouble-maker. Jesus knew the danger that faced him. He told his twelve followers:
'We are going to Jerusalem where I shall be given up to the chief priests and their lawyers, condemned to death, handed over to the Romans, mocked, flogged and crucified. But on the third day I shall be raised to life again.'
     Soon Jesus and the twelve disciples were only a few miles from Jerusalem. They came to a small village called Bethany near the Mount of Olives. Jesus told two of his disciples to go into the village saying that they would find there a donkey with her foal. They should untie them and bring them back. If

anyone objected they should simply say: The Master needs them. The owner would let them take the donkeys.

It was as Jesus said. The two disciples put their cloaks over the animals and Jesus rode down the hill to Jerusalem. As he passed through the gates of the city, the people welcomed him, cheering and tearing branches off the palm trees to wave and to throw down before the donkey. Perhaps some of them thought Jesus was the Messiah, the one who would free men from their sins, perhaps some of them thought he would lead an army against the Romans and free the Jewish nation. All was excitement and happiness.

But as Jesus passed through the gates into the city of Jerusalem some of the Pharisees were watching him. They were very strict religious people. They did not like Jesus because he could see that they weren't as good as they seemed – and he told everybody so. The Pharisees asked the crowd:

'Who is this man?'

'It's the prophet, Jesus of Nazareth.'

'If it's only him, what's all the noise about? Stop this shouting.'

But Jesus heard them grumbling:

'If the people stopped shouting, the stones beneath your feet would cry out!'

Jesus went right to the centre of the city where the great Temple of Jerusalem stood. The Temple was a beautiful building, surrounded by open-air courtyards where there were stalls selling pigeons for sacrifice and places where foreigners could change money. It was more like a marketplace than a temple with the buying and selling and the shouting and noise. Jesus marched in and angrily threw over the stalls:

'God's house is a house of prayer; you are turning it into a den of thieves.'

The Pharisees watched, seething with anger. It was no use trying to do anything now: Jesus had all the people on his side. They would wait and they would plan. Their turn would come – they weren't going to let a carpenter's son from Nazareth get the better of them for long.

*

Jesus often had harsh things to say about the Pharisees. They paraded their 'goodness'. When they prayed they did so loudly so everyone would be impressed. Jesus said:

In your prayers don't go babbling on as the pagans do, thinking that the more they say the better God will hear them. Don't be like them; God is your Father and he already knows what you need before you ask him. This is how you should pray:

Our Father in heaven,
May your name be kept holy,
May your kingdom come,

May your will be done on earth as it is in heaven.
Give us today the food we need;
Forgive us the wrongs we have done
As we have forgiven people who have wronged us.
And do not put us to the test
But save us from evil

For if you forgive others the wrongs they have done you, your heavenly Father will also forgive you. But if you do not forgive others, then the wrongs you have done will not be forgiven by the Father.

(from the Gospel of St. Matthew, late 1st century CE)

Maundy Thursday

late March/April

Maundy Thursday is the Thursday before Easter (q.v.) and is associated with the last supper Jesus shared with his twelve followers before his crucifixion. It was the first meal of the Jewish Feast of the Passover (q.v.), celebrating the deliverance of the Jews from their Egyptian slavery. The bread eaten is unleavened (contains no yeast) because the Israelites in their hurry to flee Egypt had no time to prepare it properly. Christian churches today vary as to their interpretation of the Last Supper – the Roman Catholic Church considers the bread and wine to transubstantiate (actually change) into the body and blood of Christ during the re-enactment of the meal, while most Protestant churches hold the bread and wine to be a symbol. Some Churches hold the service several times weekly, others rarely. It was known by the early Christians as the 'love-feast' and is now variously called the Lord's Supper, Holy Communion, Eucharist or Mass.

Before the Last Supper Jesus washed the feet of his disciples as a sign of fellowship. Servants would often wash the feet of their masters. Medieval kings washed the feet of the poor on Maundy Thursday. The British monarch gives 'Maundy Money', minted for the purpose, to as many old people as the sovereign is years old. The word 'maundy' derives from the Latin 'dies mandati' i.e. 'the day of Jesus's mandate' to love one another as he loved them.

Jesus's Last Supper with his Disciples   (7 min.)

Jesus had gone to the city of Jerusalem for the great Jewish festival of the Passover. The city was crowded with Jews from places near and far. Jesus had ridden humbly into the city on a donkey, but the people had cheered him and thrown palm branches in his path. Each day Jesus had been to the Temple to pray and to preach, and crowds had gathered to hear him. Among the crowds were always some of Jesus's enemies. They tried to trick him in arguments to make him look silly. But it was his enemies who were laughed at, and of course this made them angrier than ever. They had a plan to get rid of Jesus once and for all – and it was nearly time to carry it out.

*

One of his enemies asked Jesus if the Jews should pay tax to the Roman emperor. If Jesus said 'yes', he knew the people would not be very pleased because their Roman overlords were hated; if he said 'no', the Romans would have to take action against him. It seemed that Jesus was caught whatever he said. But Jesus was not afraid to give an answer:

'Shame on you. You say one thing and mean something else. Why are you trying to catch me out? Show me the money in which the tax is paid.'

They handed him a silver piece.

'Whose head is on this coin?'

'Caesar's,' replied the crowd.

'Then pay Caesar what is due to Caesar, and pay God what is due to God.'

Many tried to trick Jesus, but none succeeded. He won many friends when he went to speak in the Temple, but his enemies grew more impatient for his death.

*

One of Jesus's followers was Judas Iscariot and his job with the disciples had always been to look after the money they shared. On the day before the Feast of the Passover was due to begin, Judas secretly went to the chief priests who offered him thirty pieces of silver if he would betray Jesus to them. He went back without telling anyone where he had been.

Jesus arranged with his disciples to eat the first meal of the Passover together. Usually the Passover is a time when Jewish families get together for rejoicing, but Jesus was a religious leader so it was natural that he should want to spend the time with his followers. Jesus sent his disciples into the city to hire a room where they could eat and told them to get everything ready for the meal.

That evening Jesus met his twelve followers in the hired room.

*

Before supper Jesus rolled up his sleeves, took a towel and filled a basin with water. He washed and then dried the feet of each of his disciples. His followers did not understand what he was doing; only servants and slaves washed their master's feet, but Jesus was their master. Why should he be washing their feet?

When it came to Peter's turn, he refused:

'You, Lord, washing my feet? I will never let you wash my feet.'

'If I do not wash your feet,' said Jesus, 'how can you be a friend of mine?'

'In that case,' replied Peter, 'wash not only my feet, but my hands and head as well.'

When Jesus had finished, he explained what he had done. He was showing them that if he, their master, could stoop down and wash their feet, they should never be too proud to serve other people. He wanted his followers to love other people as much as he had loved them.

As they all sat down to eat the meal Jesus said that one of them was going to betray him. The end was near for him. The disciples couldn't believe it. They knew that Jesus' enemies were closing in on him; they were afraid for him every time he went to the Temple and preached; they had heard Jesus say that he would be taken and killed – but now he said that one of *them* was going to hand him over! Who could it be? Each one wondered if it could be he.

As they were eating Jesus took the bread, said the blessing, broke the bread and gave it to his disciples with the words:

'This is my body which is given for you; do this in memory of me.'

Then he poured out the wine, saying:

'Drink from it, all of you. For this is my blood, shed for many for the forgiveness of sins.'

When the meal was over, they all sang the Passover hymn, and then got ready to leave. Judas Iscariot left first. Jesus and the eleven disciples went out of the house and towards the Mount of Olives. As they walked in the darkness Jesus said:

'I am like a shepherd. If the shepherd is struck down, his sheep all scatter and leave him. Tonight you will be like the sheep. But I will be raised again and be with you.'

They went to the garden of Gethsemane on the slopes of the Mount of Olives. Jesus was going to pray there in the quiet and peace of the garden. Down in the city Judas Iscariot was talking with the chief priests and their soldiers.

*

Jesus taught many things but one of his sayings sums up many of the others:

'This is the most important commandment of all,' said Jesus. 'The Lord our

God is only one Lord. Love the Lord your God with all your heart, with all your soul, with all your mind, and with all your strength. The second most important commandment is this: Love your neighbour as yourself. There are no other commandments greater than these.' (from the Gospel of St. Mark, *c*.68 CE)

Good Friday

late March/April

Falling on the Friday before Easter (q.v.) the anniversary of the death of Jesus of Nazareth is the most solemn festival of the Christian year. On this day Jesus was crucified by his enemies and, as God incarnate, thus redeemed the sins of men that they might be saved from eternal damnation in hell.

Crucifixion was the punishment for a number of offences under the Roman Empire: it entailed the nailing of the hands and feet of the victim to a wooden cross where he was left to die. Wine was offered to deaden the pain but Jesus refused it. Although the trial was conducted by Jewish priests, only the Roman governor, Pontius Pilatus, was empowered to order the death penalty. Speed was essential for the priests, who had to have the execution carried out before the Jewish sabbath which begins at sunset on Friday, and so the trial continued throughout the previous night.

Special services are held on this day and the purple veils with which some churches cover the crucifix during Passiontide are removed (Passion Sunday is the fifth Sunday of Lent and two weeks before Easter). Coverings on other pictures and images are removed on Holy Saturday in preparation for Easter. Spicy bread buns marked with a pastry cross are eaten on this day in memory of the crucifixion.

The Death of Jesus   (7 min.)

While Jesus prayed in the quietness of the Garden of Gethsemane, Judas was being paid thirty pieces of silver for volunteering to lead the soldiers to arrest him. Jesus knew what would happen to him and had told the disciples that they could not keep faith with him even for that one night.

'That may be true of the others,' said Peter, 'but I will stand by you.'

'Before the cock crows three times, Peter,' Jesus told him, 'you will have pretended three times that you don't even know me.'

'I'd rather die. I will never let you down.'

Jesus prayed in the garden:

'Father, don't let me suffer this. But if it is your wish, I will do it.'

Jesus turned to his disciples; they had all fallen asleep. When he woke them they were ashamed and promised to stay awake. Again Jesus prayed:

'Father, if I have to suffer this, then I must, because it is your will.'

A second time the disciples had gone to sleep. This time Jesus left them sleeping and prayed yet again. When he had finished he woke the disciples.

'Still sleeping? The hour has come. The Son of Man has been betrayed to sinful men. Get up! The traitor is here!'

At that moment Judas appeared with the soldiers of the Temple guard carrying torches and swords and clubs. Judas had told the soldiers that the man he went up to and kissed on both cheeks was their man.

'You don't need your swords; I'm not a bandit. Besides I've been down to the Temple every day, why didn't you arrest me there?'

Jesus turned to the disciples, but they had run away, every one.

*

After he had been arrested Jesus was taken for questioning to the house of the Chief Priest. Outside Peter waited. A serving girl said to him:

'Aren't you one of those with Jesus of Galilee?'

'I don't know who you mean,' said Peter quickly, and he went out of the gate. As he came out another girl said:

'This man was with Jesus of Nazareth.'

'I don't even know the man,' answered Peter crossly.

Later some people standing by asked Peter:

'Surely you're another of that lot from Galilee, with Jesus? We can tell by the way you talk.'

Peter started arguing angrily with them, and, as he did so, a cock crowed three times. When he remembered what Jesus had said, Peter wept bitterly.

Inside the house the priests had had enough of questioning and took Jesus before the Roman governor. They said that Jesus was guilty of causing trouble and calling himself King of the Jews.

'Are you a king?' asked Pilate, the Roman governor.

'You used the word, not me,' said Jesus.

Pilate was cross with the priests; they had no real case against Jesus.

'I can't find anything wrong with this man. I shall let him off with a flogging. Wait! – it's my custom at this time of year to free one prisoner for the Jews. I shall ask the people to set this Jesus free. He has done nothing wrong.'

Pilate went to the crowds outside his palace and called to the people below, but the priests had already put their supporters among them.

'Crucify him! Crucify him!' the priests' men shouted.

'Crucify him!' shouted the people. Soon the whole crowd was demanding the death of Jesus. Not wanting trouble Pilate handed Jesus over to his soldiers to be taken for execution.

First Jesus was flogged. Then the soldiers, laughing, dressed him up like a king – a red robe on his back, a stick in his hand for a sceptre and a crown of thorns pressed down on his head. They bowed low before him and joked:

'Hail, King of the Jews.'

And they spat on him and beat him. Carrying his own wooden crossbar, Jesus was led to the place of execution outside the city, where his hands and feet were nailed to the crossbar. The cross was put in position and a notice was nailed on the top which read: This is Jesus, the King of the Jews.

As Jesus hung from the cross he called out to God:

'Father, forgive them; they don't know what they're doing.'

At the foot of the cross, the people jeered and mocked and laughed, and the soldiers gambled for his clothes. It was midday. Then a darkness came over the whole land as the sun was eclipsed. For three hours the darkness lasted until Jesus called out:

'Father, take my spirit into your hands.'

The Roman officer looked up and said, as Jesus died:

'Truly, this man was the Son of God.'

*

As evening fell a rich friend of Jesus, Joseph of Arimethea, went to Pilate to ask if he could take the body to be buried. Pilate gave the orders and the body of Jesus was handed over to Joseph who took it to his own tomb, a cave in the rock.

The priests came complaining to Pilate:

'It was prophesied that this Jesus would come to life three days after his execution. We must have your permission to block up the mouth of the tomb. If we don't, his disciples will steal away the body and pretend that he's alive again.'

Permission was given and a huge boulder was rolled across the cave mouth and a guard of temple soldiers was left to keep watch.

*

Jesus said:

'When a man believes in me, he believes in Him who sent me rather than in me; when he sees me, he sees Him who sent me. I came as a light into the world, so that whoever believes in me shall not live in darkness. But if anyone hears my words and pays no attention to them, I shall not judge him: I didn't come to judge the world but to save the world.' (from the Gospel of St. John, late 1st century CE)

Easter Sunday

late March/April

Easter (perhaps named after an Anglo-Saxon goddess of spring) was a pre-Christian festival marking the end of winter. It is now one of the high points of the Christian year being the anniversary of the return of Jesus Christ from the dead. This essential part of Christian dogma promises life after death to mankind through this event.

Easter is a movable feast, calculated according to rather complex rules using a hypothetical moon, and can fall anywhere between 22 March and 25 April. Shrove Tuesday, Ash Wednesday, Ascension Day, and Whit Sunday all move their dates in relation to Easter. The festival is celebrated by Western and Eastern churches on the same date.

Easter is a time of great rejoicing for Christians but it does not have the same secular connotations in the west as Christmas (q.v.). Special church services are held, images and statues covered since Passion Sunday are revealed, and churches are often decorated with flowers. Easter has always been associated with the coming of spring and the rebirth of nature. In Britain chocolate eggs are given to children as an ancient symbol of new life. Some few customs such as rolling eggs down hills still survive.

The Resurrection of Jesus   (4 min.)

Jesus had been crucified and Joseph of Arimethea, a rich follower of his, had taken the body to be laid in his own tomb. The priests were afraid that the disciples might steal the body and pretend that Jesus had risen from the dead. They had ordered that a huge stone be rolled across the mouth of the cave. Saturday, the Jewish holy day, had passed, and it was now the early morning of Sunday.

Mary, a friend of Jesus, and another Mary, the mother of two of the disciples, walked sadly to the grave. The place where the body had lain was empty. Inside the tomb was an angel who told them that Jesus had risen from the dead.

They started to run back to where the disciples were staying, not knowing whether to laugh or cry. And as they ran away they saw a man standing in their path. When they looked into his face they saw at once that it was Jesus. The angel had been right: the man that had been put to death three days before was standing here alive before them. Jesus had conquered death.

Jesus calmed them in their excitement and fear and gave them a message for his disciples. He would meet them all in Galilee and they should set out for that place straightaway.

Full of joy the eleven disciples travelled back to Galilee, to the mountain where Jesus had told them to meet, and when they saw him, they fell on their knees because they now knew for sure that Jesus was God on earth.

He told them:

'Go forth and make all nations my disciples; baptise men everywhere in the name of the Father and of the Son and of the Holy Spirit, and teach them all that I have taught you. And be sure of this: I am with you always, to the end of time.'

*

Many people think of Jesus as the light which shines in a dark and ignorant world. At a time when Christians were being attacked in Rome and elsewhere, one Christian wrote:

'Let us shake off the ignorance and darkness that spreads like mist over our eyes and let us really see the true God. Let us sing a hymn of praise to the God of Light. We lay buried in darkness and shut up in the shadow of death, when a light shone out from heaven, a light purer than the sun and sweeter than the life of earth. That light is everlasting life, and whoever shares in it will live. Night shrinks back from the light and gives place to the day of the Lord.' (from 'Encouragement' by Clement of Alexandria, 2nd century CE)

Ascension Day

late April/May/early June

Ascension Day marks the return to heaven of Jesus after his resurrection 40 days earlier on Easter Sunday (q.v.). It was prophesied by an angel who appeared after his ascension that Jesus would return to mankind at some future date in the same way as he departed, and some Christian sects, particularly the Adventists, many of whom are to be found amongst West Indians, hold this as one of the prominent features of their faith.

A tradition of decorating or dressing wells with floral biblical pictures has survived in the Derbyshire Peak District of England. The tradition probably dates back to the Celts to whom certain wells, pools or lakes were held sacred. Many examples of votive offerings have been found in such places and the continuing custom of throwing coins into wishing wells is a degenerate form of this worship.

Jesus and Peter   (3 min.)

After he had risen from the dead Jesus appeared a number of times to the disciples. One night Peter, Thomas, James, and John were fishing on the Sea of Galilee. Though they had fished for hours they had caught nothing at all. As the sun came up they could see a man standing on the beach. Smoke was rising from a fire he had made.

'Friends, haven't you caught anything?' he asked.

They told him they hadn't.

'Cast out your net on the other side of the boat and you'll catch something.'

They muttered to each other in disbelief – after all they were fishermen and knew what they were doing. But they thought they might as well try one last time. Pulling at the net a few seconds later they found they couldn't even haul it into the boat. They dragged their great catch of fish towards the shore, and as they came nearer, they recognised Jesus.

As soon as he knew who it was, Peter dived into the sea to swim the last few hundred metres to shore. As the others landed they saw that Jesus had started cooking a breakfast of bread and fish for them.

When they had all eaten, Jesus asked Peter:

'Peter, do you love me more than anything else?'

'Yes, Lord, you know I do.'

'Then feed my lambs.'

Again Jesus said:

'Peter, do you love me?'

'Yes, Lord, you know I do.'

'Then look after my sheep.'

When Jesus asked the same question a third time, Peter was upset:

'Yes, Lord, you know everything. You know I love you.'

'Then feed my sheep.'

It seemed to some that Jesus was giving the task of leading the disciples to Peter. Many people today look on Peter as the first leader of the Christian Church.

Jesus Ascends into Heaven   (2 min.)

Jesus met and talked to his friends for forty days after he came back from the dead. When they were all together some of them asked:

'Lord are you going to make your kingdom in Israel now?'

They still thought of Jesus as being a king on earth like other kings. But Jesus answered:

'It isn't for you to know when and where the Kingdom of God will be. God's got everything under his control. But the time will come when God will fill you with his Holy Spirit and you will set out to preach my message of love all over the world.'

Jesus then walked with his disciples to the Mount of Olives near the village of Bethany and the disciples watched silently and in amazement as Jesus began to rise up into the sky. As they watched he seemed to be lifted up on a cloud until he passed out of their sight. Full of excitement and wonder they went back to the Temple in Jerusalem where they sang praises to God.

Whitsun

May/early June

Whit Sunday is the Sunday after Ascension Day (q.v.) and the fifth Sunday after Easter Day (q.v.). It fell on the Day of Pentecost, the first day of the Jewish Feast of Weeks (Pentecost means fifty in Greek – the Feast of Weeks [q.v.] comes fifty days after the second day of the Feast of the Passover [q.v.]). The disciples were filled with the Holy Spirit and were initially able to understand and speak in the languages of all the foreigners in Jerusalem. The Holy Spirit is the third person or aspect of the Christian understanding of God; God the Father, creator and ruler of the world being the first person, and Jesus Christ the Son, the divine man through whom we can reach the Deity being the second. To Christians God is one, an indivisible Trinity.

The name Whitsun derives from White Sunday, so called because this day was formerly reserved for the baptism of new converts, Jesus having called the coming of the Holy Spirit to his disciples a 'baptism'. Those to be baptised wore white robes, white being a symbol of purity.

Jesus's Disciples Receive the Holy Spirit   (5 min.)

Before Jesus had left the disciples, on the Mount of Olives, he had told them to stay in Jerusalem. He had reminded them of what John the Baptist had said when he had baptised Jesus in the waters of the River Jordan:

'I baptise you with water, but the one who comes after me is mightier than I – he will baptise you with the Holy Spirit.'

Jesus told his disciples that before long they would be filled with the Holy Spirit of God.

All the disciples of Jesus were in Jerusalem, together with several friends, Mary, Jesus's mother, some relations and a number of other followers, over a hundred in all. Peter spoke to them all on the Jewish festival of the Day of Pentecost:

'There were twelve of us. Judas, who led the enemies of Jesus and betrayed him is dead and we are now eleven. One more must be chosen.'

They chose as the new disciple a man named Matthias. Now there were twelve again. The twelve were gathered together later on the Day of Pentecost when they heard a sound in the room like a strong and rushing wind. It howled and raged but the lamps were not blown out. As they sat there in wonder the Holy Spirit came down upon them in the shape of tongues of fire which seemed to rest on the head of every disciple.

The disciples rushed out into the streets of Jerusalem. The streets were crowded because of the festival and many Jews were in the city from different countries, speaking different languages. The disciples spoke to the people telling what had happened. And everyone could understand. Wherever they were from, whatever language they spoke, the people could understand the disciples perfectly. Some thought the disciples were drunk. Eventually Peter stopped all the noise and commotion and spoke to the people:

'Friends, some say we are drunk. No, we are not drunk, it's too early in the morning. We are filled with the Holy Spirit of God as Jesus promised. This Jesus, the Son of God sent down by God to you, the man you tried, mocked and crucified, this Christ who came to save the people of the world.'

Many people were moved and upset by Peter's words:

'What shall we do?' they shouted.

'Repent,' cried Peter. 'Say you're sorry to God for the wrong you've done, and be baptised in the name of Jesus.'

That day some three thousand people became the first Christians. Day by day the disciples of Jesus talked to people and made them believe. Day by day new people were baptised Christians. The twelve met together and went to the temple to praise God; every day they joyfully shared their meals together and became the friends of all the people. They all helped one another. Where any were poor, the other Christians shared what they had. Day by day the number of Christians grew and grew.

Soon after Pentecost the disciples set out to many countries to preach Jesus's message. Some of the people from foreign countries who had been baptised in Jerusalem went home and told their friends about it. Some of them died, as Jesus had died, because not everyone could accept the message. But the Christian faith went on growing and there are now perhaps 900,000,000 Christians throughout the world.

*

O God
You are the light of the minds that know you,
The life of the souls that love you,
The strength of the hearts that serve you.
Help us to know you so we may truly love you,
Help us to love you so we may fully serve you
And in serving you find perfect freedom.
Through Jesus Christ our Lord.
Amen

(from St. Augustine of Hippo, 354–430 CE)

The Feast Day of St. Alban

22 June

Albanus or Alban was born in Verulamium (now St. Albans, Hertfordshire), a city of importance in Roman Britain from the first century. It was the only British city to achieve the status of a 'Municipium' whereby its inhabitants had the rights of Roman citizenship. Being an unwalled non-military commercial centre the city had been easy prey for Boudicca (Boadicea), Queen of the Iceni who sacked the town in 61 CE. By Alban's time it was once more a thriving and wealthy town. Alban has the distinction of being the first British Christian martyr and he shares his feast day with Amphibalus, the Christian priest he saved. Diocletian feared the Christians as a state within the state and his measures against them became more extreme as martyrdom seemed to strengthen them as the unity of the Empire weakened. Amphibalus and some followers were later captured despite Alban's help and were stoned to death at Redbourn, Hertfordshire.

St. Alban, the First British Martyr   (7 min.)

Near London is the town of St. Albans. In Roman times its name was Verulamium and the city was one of the richest and most important in Roman Britain. The villas where the rich and the noble people lived were large and beautiful. They had many rooms, and gardens with pools and fountains. There were slaves and servants to do all the work. In one of these magnificent houses lived a wealthy young man called Alban.

Alban had been born in Verulamium so he was British, but as his father had been a Roman citizen, Alban too had the honour of being a citizen of Rome. Alban's father was so rich that he had sent his son to school in Rome. Alban had then been an officer in the Roman army for some time, but now he lived in his own town in Britain again.

Although he was very rich and lived in luxury, Alban was not a mean man. He was faithful to his friends and always ready to give help; he was good to the poor and often gave them money, clothes or food when they were in need. He was known throughout the town as a good man.

Alban worshipped the Roman gods. He believed that there were many gods. He prayed to the god Mars when he was in battle, he prayed to spirits called the Lares to protect his home and to the Penates to keep his food cupboards full. He prayed to Neptune, god of the sea when he went by ship, and worshipped the king of the gods, Jupiter. On special days Alban would go to the temple and sacrifice an animal to please the gods. The Romans did not love their gods – they made a bargain with them: if the worshipper did what the god wanted and pleased him, that god would bring him good luck. So it was dangerous to make the gods angry.

Most Romans believed that the Emperor was a god on earth. Some Romans believed that there were no gods at all, some believed that there was a life after death, some believed in foreign gods, but there were a few who believed that there was only one God, a God of love who came down to earth and was murdered, crucified, but rose from the dead. When he lived on earth he was called Jesus Christ. His followers were called Christians and they were causing trouble in the Roman Empire because they refused to worship the Emperor.

Now Alban had heard about the Christians, but he had never met one. One evening, as he was strolling in his garden, he heard a shout and a clatter of feet outside in the street. There were shouts further away. Then the door from the street into Alban's garden burst open and a man rushed in shutting the door behind him. The man was old, dressed in ragged poor clothes and was so out of breath that he could not speak. Alban went up to him and took him to sit down.

'Are the soldiers chasing you?' asked Alban. 'What can they want with an old man like you?'

'I am a Christian,' said the old man. 'The Emperor has ordered the soldiers to put us all to death.'

'Well, I've certainly heard some curious stories about you Christians, but I've never heard that you harmed anyone. Come in and rest for a while and you can tell me about yourself.'

Alban took the old man, Amphibalus, into his house and cleaned him up and fed him. Then Amphibalus told Alban about himself. He was a Christian priest and he knew that if the soldiers caught him they would order him to worship the Emperor.

'There is only one God,' said Amphibalus. 'I cannot worship the Emperor – he's just a man. So I would be put to death.'

Amphibalus told Alban the story of Jesus of Nazareth, how he was put to death and how Christians believe that he rose again from the dead. Amphibalus stayed with Alban for a few days teaching him all about Christianity until Alban felt he was beginning to understand about God. One day a servant dashed into the room to tell Alban that the soldiers had started to search all the houses. They were looking for a Christian priest who had run away. Alban could hear the soldiers outside. A heavy knock came on the door.

Amphibalus stood up:

'You'll have to tell them I am here. I am too old to run.'

'No. Fetch your old cloak and put on my best one. They don't know what you look like. I'll lead them away.'

'You mustn't do this for me,' said Amphibalus.

'Yes I must. You've got a job to do, telling people about Jesus. Now, quickly.'

So they changed cloaks. As the soldiers came in they saw a man dressed in a very fine cloak sitting at a table. This must be the man who owns the house, they thought. But through the window, escaping out of the garden gate was a man with an old cloak on.

'The Christian! After him!' they cried.

After a long chase the soldiers caught Alban and dragged him before the governor. As soon as the governor saw Alban he recognised him. He was amazed to find him helping a Christian.

'Well, Alban, you're going to be in trouble alright. I'll do what I can for you, my friend, but you'll have to help. You'll have to come with me to the temple to make a sacrifice to our god the Emperor just to prove *you're* not a Christian too, and then I'll see what I can do.'

'The Emperor's no god. There is only one God that I will worship – the one and only God.'

The governor was furious. He ordered Albans' execution. With an escort of soldiers and a crowd that grew bigger as they went through the city, Alban was taken across the little river and up on to a low hill. Many people wept because everyone felt Alban was a friend. One soldier refused to take part in the execution, so the officer drew his own sword and struck off Alban's head. By helping an old Christian priest Alban became the first person in Britain to die for the Christian faith. Some years later Alban was made Saint Alban and the town of Verulamium took the name it has had ever since – St. Albans.

Feast Day of John the Baptist

24 June

John the Baptist is recognised by Christians as the last Jewish prophet to pave the way for the message of Jesus Christ, the human incarnation of the Son of God. John was born not long before Jesus (see Advent) and baptised him in the River Jordan (see Pancake Tuesday).

The Death of John the Baptist   (5 min.)

John the Baptist was a Jewish prophet who was not afraid to say what he thought. He thought that the ordinary Jewish people were leading lives of wickedness and sin and forgetting all about God. He thought that the tax-collectors cheated the ordinary people; he thought that the soldiers were bullies and hooligans; and he thought that the government and the King were sinful and cruel; he thought that the Queen was particularly evil.

People flocked to hear him. Many were baptised by John in the waters of the River Jordan and they promised to try and lead better lives. Even the soldiers and the tax-collectors came to listen. King Herod did not come: he had spies who told him all that John said and the news they brought back worried the King. It seemed to him that John was a traitor who was trying to turn people against the government, a man who must be stopped before he went any further.

When King Herod's spies brought back the news that John was preaching against the King himself, calling him a wicked sinner and not fit to be king, he decided that the time had come at last to have John arrested.

Soldiers were sent and John was brought back in chains to Jerusalem where he was thrown into prison.

But while John was in prison Herod visited him and listened to him. He found that he wasn't the troublemaker he had believed him to be; in fact he found him to be a good and honest man and began to take note of what he said.

Some time later King Herod ordered the preparation of a great feast. Many important people were invited, for it was his birthday. The banquet was magnificent and the guests enjoyed themselves tremendously. After the eating came the entertainment. One of the items was a dance by the daughter of Herod's wife, Queen Herodias. She danced so wonderfully and received such applause that Herod told her to choose her own reward. The audience were delighted.

'You have danced so well, Salome, you may have anything that it is in my power to give. Even half my kingdom. Ask for whatever you like.'

Prompted by her mother, the girl replied:

'I want the head of John the Baptist brought to me on a plate.'

Herod felt sick at heart. But he realised there was no way out. He had not the slightest wish to have John put to death, but he had made a promise to Salome in front of many people and could not go back on his word.

The executioner was sent down to the cells. Some time later he returned carrying a great silver meat plate on which was the head of John the Baptist.

But John would not have felt that he died for nothing: he had prepared the people for the coming of Jesus and his task was over now that Jesus was with them.

                    *

Jesus often spoke about death:

'Don't fear those who can kill you – after that there is nothing more they can do. I will warn you who to fear: fear Him who can kill you and cast you into hell. Believe me, He is the one to fear.

Can't you buy five sparrows for two pence? And yet God knows every one of them. More than that – every hair on your head has been counted. Have no fear – you are worth more than any number of sparrows.'

(from the Gospel of St. Luke, late 1st century CE)

St. Swithun's Day

15 July

Swithun (800–862) was Bishop of Winchester, the capital of Wessex. He had been teacher to the future King Alfred the Great. The tradition of the 40 days of rain is said to date back to the time when Swithun was canonised in 971 CE. Prophesying the weather at this time of year dates back to pagan times. However, there are many Christianised sayings on the subject:

St. Medard's Day 8 June
St. Medard's drops drop for 40 days.

St. Vitus's Day 15 June
If St. Vitus's Day be rainy weather
It will rain for 30 days together.

St. Calais's Day 1 July
If the first of July be rainy weather
'Twill rain more or less for four weeks together.

St. Swithun's Day 15 July
If St. Swithun weeps the proverb says
The weather will be foul for 40 days.

St. Swithun   (4 min.)

Bishop Swithun lived in Winchester in the time of King Alfred the Great. There are many legends about miracles that the bishop is supposed to have performed to help the people of the city. Whether they are true or not, they do show that the people of Winchester liked Swithun so much that the stories were told again and again.

One story tells of St. Swithun and the old lady who broke some eggs. An old lady taking her eggs to Winchester market one day had to cross the bridge over the river. It was only a narrow bridge and very crowded on market day. As the old lady hobbled slowly across with her basket of eggs she was bumped and jostled so much that she dropped the basket. The eggs rolled out and many were smashed. Bishop Swithun happened to be passing and knelt down to help the old lady pick up her eggs. When he had finished the lady looked in her basket and there lay all the eggs with not a single one broken.

*

Before he died the Bishop asked that he should not be buried inside the great cathedral with the nobility and the other bishops. Swithun had spent his life with ordinary people and he wanted to be buried in the churchyard with them. He thought that the sky would be a better roof for him than the stone of the great cathedral. When the beloved bishop died he had his wish.

Everyone thought so much of Bishop Swithun that his stories were still told years after his death. Eventually the Pope declared that Swithun should be made a saint. Bishop Ethelwold of Winchester decided that a saint ought to have a special grave – not an ordinary one outside the church with the common people of the city. Now that Swithun was a saint he could have a place of honour inside the great cathedral of Winchester. A ceremony and procession was arranged to take the coffin from the churchyard to a special burial place inside the cathedral. The date was fixed as 15 July and grand preparations were made.

On 15 July, when Saint Swithun's body was to be moved, the sky clouded over and heavy rain began to fall. It rained and it rained. It rained all that day and all the next. Each day Bishop Ethelwold looked out of his window to see if the weather was fit to move the saint, but still it rained. It rained for forty days. After forty days of rain the bishop decided that it was a sign to leave the saint where he was – outside with the ordinary people of the city of Winchester.

An old rhyme tells of St. Swithun's day:

St. Swithun's Day if thou dost rain,
For forty days it will remain;
St. Swithun's Day if thou be fair
For forty days 'twill rain no mair.

Since Bishop Swithun's time the cathedral at Winchester has been made bigger and now covers his grave. There is no tomb there now, but a stone marks the place where the saint's body still lies buried.

St. Andrew's Day

30 November

Andrew was one of the twelve Apostles of Jesus. He was the brother of St. (Simon) Peter who is generally recognised as the first Pope. The date of Andrew's birth is not known, but he is believed to have died about 65 CE at the hands of the Roman proconsul at Achaia, at Patraea (now in Greece). Andrew is the patron saint of Greece and Scotland, and of fishermen. The English Church commemorates St. Andrew as the first Christian missionary. The legend of Andrew's death apparently dates from mediaeval times.

Andrew Becomes a Disciple of Jesus   (2 min.)

Jesus had not been preaching for very long, but already he was famous in the country of Galilee where he lived. Many people said that Jesus was the Messiah. Whenever Jesus talked crowds would gather round to listen.

Two brothers, Simon and Andrew, were standing by the shore fishing. They had large nets which they cast out from the shore and slowly dragged back. They had heard of a new preacher, called Jesus, and talked about him, but they had never seen him or heard him speak. As they patiently threw their nets out and pulled them in again, they noticed a man walking slowly along the shore of the lake. He came up to them and stopped to watch.

Andrew and Simon Peter stopped fishing and turned to look at the stranger. Jesus spoke:

'Come with me, and I will make you fishers of men.'

Andrew and Simon simply did as they were told. They left their nets on the edge of the lake and went with Jesus.

A little bit further along the shore there were more fishermen. Zebedee and his two sons, James and John, were sitting in the boat mending their nets. Jesus said to James and John:

'Come with me; from now on you will be catching not fish, but men.'

And they too left their father and their fishing nets and went with Jesus. Andrew, Simon, James, and John became the first disciples.

The Feeding of Five Thousand People   (3 min.)

Jesus travelled all around the country preaching to crowds of people wherever he went. At the same time he was teaching the twelve disciples his message, so that one day they would be able to carry on without him. On one of his journeys round the villages Jesus called the disciples together and told them that they were to go off in twos to preach on their own. James and John went off together. So did Andrew and Simon, and the others of the twelve. Jesus arranged to meet them all back at the shores of the Sea of Galilee.

After several days they all met up again. Jesus said that they would find a quiet place away from the crowds where they could rest after their hard work. They set off in a boat across the Sea of Galilee. But the people saw them leave, told others, followed the boat round the shores of the lake and were already waiting when the disciples landed. Jesus didn't have the heart to send them away. He said to the disciples:

'They are like sheep without a shepherd: I must speak to them.'

As evening began to fall, the disciples came to Jesus. Andrew said:

'It's getting rather late, Lord, and this is a lonely place. Hadn't you better send these people off to the villages and farms round about to get themselves something to eat?'

'Give them something to eat yourselves,' said Jesus.

'How can we? We haven't got enough money to buy food for this lot,' answered Andrew. 'There must be thousands of people here!'

'How much food have we got?' asked Jesus. 'You'd better go and see.'

Andrew and the other disciples asked the people. Nobody, it seemed, had brought any food. Then one small boy offered the disciples five small loaves of bread and two fishes. Andrew gave the food to Jesus, who took it and blessed it and began to share it amongst the people. When everyone had as much as they wanted to eat, there was enough food left over to fill twelve baskets.

The crowd started to talk about Jesus. Some said that Jesus was the Messiah. Some said that they ought to proclaim him King of the Jews. Jesus knew this, but he was to be no earthly king. When darkness fell, Jesus and the twelve disciples went off in their boat, back across the Sea of Galilee.

Andrew's Death   (4 min.)

After the resurrection, Jesus told his twelve disciples that they were not to keep his message to themselves. They should go out and preach to all the countries of the world. Andrew travelled through many countries preaching. He went to Syria, Turkey, and up into Russia. Finally he went to Greece. In one of the provinces of Greece, Andrew spoke to the people in the market-place of the city of Patraea. In the crowd listening to him was the wife of the Roman governor of the province. When Andrew had finished speaking she asked him more about Jesus. Andrew gladly told her.

When the governor's wife got home, she was full of the story. Excitedly, she told her husband all about the Jew who had been born the Son of God. She said he had come to save all people, rich and poor alike. The governor, Aegeas, was very angry. It seemed that Andrew was not the only one going around the Roman provinces preaching Jesus's message. He regarded the followers of Jesus as trouble-makers. But the more her husband shouted, the more Aegeas's wife became convinced that Jesus was really someone special. She spent the next few days telling her friends about him too.

Aegeas was now seriously worried by all this business about Jesus. It was bad enough having this man Andrew causing trouble around the city, without having to come home and hear his wife talking about Jesus too. Aegeas sent out the order for Andrew to be arrested.

Andrew was taken to the place of execution. He was to be crucified, like Jesus – but not on the same kind of cross. Andrew was tied to a diagonal cross, and here he hung for two days in great pain. However, he knew that his message was too important to die with him. While he was suffering on the cross he preached about Jesus to the crowds who had come to laugh at him. He was so brave, and spoke so well as he hung there dying, that many of the people who heard him became Christians.

*

About 500 years after Andrew's death, at a time when the emperors of Rome had decided that everyone in the Empire should be Christian, St. Andrew's body was taken to the great city of Constantinople. By the order of the Emperor, Andrew's body was laid in a special grave and a monk was employed to look after it. The monk who was given the job was called Regulus. One night Regulus had such a vivid dream, he thought that it must be a message from God. In the dream an angel told Regulus to take Andrew's body away from Constantinople. The angel would show Regulus where the body must be reburied. So Regulus set out on his journeys. He travelled throughout the whole length of the great Roman Empire, preaching as he went. At last he came to the very edges of the known world, to a wild land where only a few warlike tribes lived, to the land we now call Scotland. Here Regulus buried the body of St. Andrew. Ever since, the place of burial has been known as St. Andrew's. And so the people of Scotland, when they became Christian, chose Andrew to be their own patron saint.

*

O Lord our God,
Whose power and mercy cannot be measured,
Look upon us and your people in your great love
And show us and those who pray with us
How great is your mercy and sympathy.
To you belong glory, power and honour,
now and for ever more.
Amen

(from the Liturgy of the Mass of the Armenian Orthodox Church)

Advent

late November/early December

Advent 'the coming' has been celebrated by the Western Christian Church since about the 6th century CE as a time of preparation for Christmas. Advent Sunday is four Sundays before Christmas Day and falls on the Sunday nearest to 30 November, St. Andrew's Day. Some Christians remember that the word 'Advent' also refers to the second coming of Jesus Christ to establish God's kingdom here. Old Testament readings in Churches remind Christians that Jesus's coming had been prophesied throughout Jewish history. Advent candles are burned and calendars are made often with flaps which are lifted day by day to reveal various aspects of the story of the nativity of Jesus Christ.

The birth of John the Baptist, whose mother was a cousin of Jesus's mother, occurred six months before that of Jesus, but is remembered here because Christians regard John as the last prophet who came to prepare the Jews for the coming of the Messiah (Greek – literally the anointed one, i.e. the deliverer of the Jews from oppression). The story of the Annunciation to the Virgin Mary (i.e. the announcing by the Archangel Gabriel to Mary that she will conceive a child) is celebrated nine months before Christmas Day on 25 March, Lady Day (q.v.), but is also remembered now.

The Birth of John the Baptist   (5 min.)

The four weeks before Christmas are the time when Christians get ready for the birth of Jesus Christ. They often remember that John the Baptist was born not many months before Jesus. John was Jesus's cousin and when he grew up he travelled around the country preaching and preparing the people for the time when Jesus would come to them.

An old priest named Zechariah was leading the service at the Temple in Jerusalem. As the people prayed, Zechariah went into the Temple to burn the sweet-smelling incense. But as he stood there a vision of the Angel Gabriel appeared to him and said:

'Do not be afraid, Zechariah; your prayer has been heard; your wife Elizabeth will bear you a son, and you shall name him John. He will prepare a way for the Lord.'

Zechariah did not believe the angel. He told him that he and his wife were old. They had never had children and now it seemed that Elizabeth was too old to have any. They couldn't possibly have a child now.

Gabriel said that because he doubted his message from God, Zechariah would not be able to speak until his son was born. The people outside in the Temple were waiting for Zechariah; he had been a long time. When he finally came out, they realised that he must have had a vision: he looked shocked and was unable to speak.

Zechariah went back home to his wife. He explained to her in signs what had happened in the Temple. Elizabeth was delighted. At last she was to have a child.

Nine months later Elizabeth's child was born. It was a boy as the Angel Gabriel had foretold. The family and relations were thrilled. They began to choose names for the boy. Most of them said he should be called Zechariah after his father, but Elizabeth said:

'No! he is to be called John.'

'But there is nobody in your family who has that name,' they said.

Zechariah was asked. The old priest wrote:

'His name is John.'

Immediately the old man found that he could speak again. Everyone was amazed and they all knew that the child must be very special.

'What will this child become?' they asked.

Zechariah replied that the child, John, would become a great prophet to the Jews, but he would only be preparing the way for the greatest of all.

*

Here are the words Zechariah used:

You, my child, shall be called the Prophet of the Highest,
for you will come before the Lord, to prepare his way
and show his people the way to be saved through him
by the forgiveness of their sins:
For in God's tender mercy
the morning sun will rise upon us
to shine on those who live in darkness in the shadow of death,
and to guide our feet into the way of peace.

(from the Gospel of St. Luke, 1st century CE)

The Feast Day of St. Nicholas

6 December

Born in Asia Minor at Patara (south-west Turkey), Nicholas gave everything he owned to charity when his wealthy parents died of the plague, and made a pilgrimage to the Holy Land. Returning to Myra, capital city of his native Lycia, he was appointed bishop. During the Roman Emperor Diocletian's persecution (303 CE) Nicholas was imprisoned. In 325 he was one of the bishops summoned to attend Emperor Constantine's first great Church Council, on doctrine, at Nicaea. He was buried at Myra. About 350 miracles were attributed to Nicholas who was later canonised. His relics were captured in 1087 and enshrined at Bari in Italy which became a centre of pilgrimage. Legends tell of Nicholas's care for the oppressed and poor; he is the patron saint of children, of sailors and travellers, of Russia. His coat-of-arms, three gold discs representing the gold bags of the story, on a blue background, is the basis of the old pawnbroker's sign.

St. Nicholas and the Three Poor Girls   (4 min.)

In the city of Myra, in the Roman Empire, there lived a poor nobleman and his three daughters in a small low house. When he had been rich there had been no need to work, but now the nobleman was poor there was no work he could do. Each day things got worse; there was less and less to eat and some days there was nothing at all. As winter came on the house grew cold and there was no fuel to heat it; the roof leaked and the doors and windows were draughty.

As the nobleman's daughters came to the age when they could marry they dreamed of rich young men marrying them and saving the family. But nobody wanted to marry a girl who had no money at all.

One night the nobleman called the girls together and told them he had found a solution to their problem.

'Daughters, you know very well how poor we are. I've no money to feed myself or keep myself warm, so I've certainly none for you. The only thing that I can possibly do, for your good as well as my own, is to sell you all as slaves.'

Gossip soon spread round the city of Myra. Nothing else was discussed in the markets and the streets, in the pubs and the shops; it was whispered in the churches. The whole city knew – the poorest peasant, the richest man, even the bishop whose name was Nicholas. Each day visitors called at the poor nobleman's small low house – some were slave-traders or rich men calling to see what price to offer for the girls, others were just nosey. Each day the three daughters grew more terrified.

Bishop Nicholas had rich parents when he was a boy, but when they died of the plague he had given all his money away to the poor. As bishop he had always cared for the people of Myra and when he heard the tale of the nobleman's daughters he decided to do something.

The end of the week was drawing near and Nicholas had to act quickly. He gathered together as much money in gold coins as he could muster and put it into three bags. The first night Nicholas secretly crept up to the home of the nobleman and, scrambling up the rough wall of the low house, dropped one bag of gold down the chimney. Inside the family awoke with a start as something came tumbling sootily down the chimney into the empty fireplace. Opening the bag, they could not believe their good luck.

A second night the same thing happened. On the third night the girls and their father were waiting. As the bag of gold clinked in the chimney for the third time, they rushed out of the house and were amazed to find their bishop about to race off down the dark street.

Bishop Nicholas swore them to secrecy, but before many days the whole city of Myra knew how much their bishop cared for the poor.

*

Bishop Nicholas became known as Saint Nicholas. He is the patron-saint of children and is remembered by children every year in England, Germany, and in Holland where they put stockings or clogs by the fireplace to receive gifts from the saint. He is known as Santa (which means Saint) Claus (short for Nicklaus) – Santa Claus.

*

This prayer was written by a Greek Christian bishop at about the time Nicholas was alive:

I thank you, glorify and praise you,
O Lord my God.
Protect me from all disasters,
Drive away all my enemies and those who would do me wrong.
Direct my thoughts, words and deeds and always be with me.
O Lover of mankind,
you are full of mercy and kindness,
You have given us everything that is good,
And to you belongs the glory with the Father and the Holy Spirit,

Now and for ever more,
World without end.
Amen

(from a Prayer of St. John Chrysostom, 347–407 CE,
from the Mass of the Armenian Orthodox Church)

Christmas

25 December

Christmas is one of the most important Christian festivals. In most parts of the United Kingdom and in many other countries it has developed into an important secular festival. Presents are given to relatives and friends, and particularly to children. Greetings cards are sent, special Christmas meals are eaten, and parties are held.

Jesus was born in Bethlehem in Judaea (now Israel) probably two years before the death in 4 BCE of Herod the Great, a Roman client king. (The dating of the Christian era from Jesus' birth was miscalculated by the Roman monk, Dionysius Exiguus in 553 CE, but the system continued so long in common use that it proved impractical to alter it). After Herod's death Judaea became a Roman province with its own procurator (Pontius Pilatus being one of the holders of this post), while Galilee was ruled by Herod's son, Herod Antipas, under Roman patronage.

Although Jesus's father was a carpenter in Nazareth in Galilee, he was travelling with his pregnant fiancée, Mary, to be registered for tax purposes in his home town of Bethlehem about six miles from Jerusalem. The Roman governor of Syria, Quirinius, had ordered the census under a decree of Emperor Augustus.

The Christmas feast lasts for twelve days from 25 December, though in the United Kingdom festivities tend to be confined to Christmas Day itself, the following day which is Boxing Day, and the weekends either side of Christmas. There is little evidence to suggest the date as being the actual birthday of Jesus and the choice seems to have established itself by the 5th century with reference to non-Christian festivals which took place on or around the shortest day, 21 December. Many non-Christian elements were retained in the celebration of the day – the decorating of house interiors with evergreens, the burning of a Yule log, and the eating of a special meal.

The Birth of Jesus   (4 min)

Joseph the carpenter lived in the town of Nazareth in Galilee. He was travelling to the town of Bethlehem where he had been born. Two thousand years ago, when you could only go by donkey or use your own legs, when the roads were bad and robbers were many, a hundred kilometres was a long way to travel. Joseph lived in a Roman province; everyone in that part of the Empire had been ordered to go back to the town where he had been born to have his name registered in a census. This was so that the Romans would know how many people should be paying tax – tax for mending the roads, building bridges, and fighting wars. Joseph might have enjoyed the journey if he had not been so worried: he had to bring his wife Mary along with him – and Mary was pregnant. She was expecting her baby any time now and Joseph thought it would have been safer to have it at home.

It was getting late in the day when they arrived and the town was crowded. They tried at many an inn for a bed, but everywhere there were people who had all come to register their names in the census. Joseph explained to the innkeepers that his wife was due to have a baby very soon – they were sorry but they just did not have a bed to give them. Joseph was getting really worried now: Mary could feel that it would not be long before the baby was born; it was very late, it was dark and they were still walking the streets.

Joseph tried at another inn:

'Have you got a bed for the night, please?'

'I'm sorry, but we're full up with people registering for the census.'

'Isn't there anywhere at all? You see, my wife's going to have a baby and she can't have it in the street!'

The innkeeper scratched his head and thought:

'Well,' he said. 'The bedrooms are full up, the rooms downstairs have people sleeping on the floor; but, if you don't mind it, there *is* room in the stable. There's dry straw in there and it's warm. You can sleep with the cow and the donkey if you like.'

Mary and Joseph thanked the innkeeper. They were delighted to be able to use the stable. That night Mary's baby was born. Mary wrapped him up and, because they had no cot, she laid him in the manger on the hay that had been put out for the animals. They called the baby, Jesus.

Not far from the stable were shepherds looking after their sheep that night. Suddenly the sky was filled with a brilliant white light and an angel appeared to them. They were terrified, but the angel spoke kindly, telling them that a baby had been born; it was no ordinary child, for it was the Son of God, the one who had come to save mankind. The angel told them they would find the baby lying in a manger. As the angel finished speaking, the heavens were filled with innumerable angels singing and praising God.

After the angels had left them the shepherds could hardly believe what had happened. But they left their flocks of sheep and went up the hill into the town. It was just as the angel had said. There was the child lying in a manger. It is said that the shepherds left a lamb as a present for the child, Jesus. As the shepherds went back to their sheep on the hills, the sky was growing light again as the sun rose on the very first Christmas Day.

*

Alleluia.   Praise God in his saints.
Alleluia.   Praise his power in the vastness of the heavens.
Alleluia.   Praise him in his mighty deeds.
Alleluia.   Praise him as greatly as he is great.
Alleluia.   Praise him with the sound of trumpets.
Alleluia.   Praise him with songs and the sound of the harp.
Alleluia.   Praise him with dancing and tambourines.
Alleluia.   Praise him with violins and organs.
Alleluia.   Praise him with crashing cymbals.
Alleluia.   Praise him with joyful cymbals.
Alleluia.   Let everything that breathes praise the name of the Lord our God.
             Alleluia.

(from the Coptic Orthodox Church – based on Psalm 150. Sung to the accompaniment of cymbals.)

Hindu Festivals

The Day of Spring (Basant Panchami)

5th of the month of Magha
February/March

Basant is the Indian festival of spring. At this time the Punjab is covered with the yellow flowers of a mustard-like vegetable, sarson. New turbans and saris are worn made up in yellow, the colour of spring and fertility (and also incidentally of bravery). Fairs, special meals, and concerts are held in the Punjab.

Other Hindus in India hold the day sacred to the goddess Sarasvati, sister of Shiva and wife of Brahma, two of the supreme triad (the other being Vishnu). Sarasvati is worshipped on this day as the patroness of the arts and sciences, and of wisdom and knowledge. Pens, brushes, and books are laid before her statue in the temples. As the goddess of learning she is especially revered by schoolchildren and students. Depicted with grace and beauty, Sarasvati is shown having four arms and holding a flower out for her husband whose constant companion she is. She also holds a book to show her love of learning, and a long stringed instrument.

Brahma is said to have created the four Vedas, the earliest Hindu scriptures. These were written down about 1,000 BCE through Sarasvati who invented the Sanskrit language. Sanskrit is the Indian counterpart of Latin in Europe, and the devanagari alphabet which is still used for Hindi today.

With approximately 350,000,000 Hindus variety is inevitable, but most Hindus worship one of the supreme triad of gods, although they take part in celebrations dedicated to gods of whom they are not particular devotees. However, the many gods and spirits and indeed the whole of creation, including mankind, are understood to be a part of the one supreme spirit of God. The multiplicity of Hindu gods are steps on the path to understanding God. All gods are aspects of the One God.

Sarasvati, Goddess of Learning   (4 min.)

To celebrate the spring festival in India, men, women and children put on new yellow clothes. The men wear a brand new turban of yellow material. The women wind a new length of yellow cloth, perhaps fifteen metres long, around them to make a sari. Yellow is the colour of spring in India because the fields and hillsides are covered with the little yellow flowers of a plant called sarson. Everyone prays that the crops they sow that year will grow well. The coming of spring is celebrated in a festival called Basant Panchami – the Day of Spring.

In some parts of India, Hindus also celebrate the day as the holy day of the goddess Sarasvati. Many schoolchildren already have a picture of Sarasvati in their desks. Sarasvati is remembered every day, as the goddess of learning, of wisdom and knowledge. The picture shows Sarasvati holding a book and a musical instrument like a long guitar, for she is also the goddess of music. On this day, Indians will go to the temples and place pens and books before her statue. They will burn sweet-smelling incense to praise her and they will sing hymns to her youth and beauty.

Sarasvati is the wife of Brahma, one of the three great gods of the Hindus. Brahma is the god who created all things, the father of gods and men. Brahma created himself and he created the universe, but there did not seem any point in existing if he had no one to share it with. So Brahma created Sarasvati. She was so young and graceful, so very beautiful that at once Brahma fell in love with her.

Entranced by her beauty, Brahma gazed at Sarasvati. The lovely goddess, overcome with shyness, moved modestly to Brahma's right. Immediately Brahma grew another head on that side. Sarasvati moved to his left to avoid his stare and the god grew a head on that side too. She ran behind him and Brahma grew a fourth head there. Finally, in despair, Sarasvati leaped into the sky. Of course Brahma grew a fifth head above all the others so that he could still look at her. Sarasvati realised Brahma loved her and they were both happy. Sarasvati gave birth to Manu, the first man in the world, and the first of the human race.

So at springtime in India Sarasvati, the mother of mankind, is remembered and praised by all Hindus.

*

Mankind came from God and so we all have a little part of God's soul within us. God is the soul within us. These words come from one of the Hindu scriptures:

God is the soul within my heart
– smaller than a grain of rice,

smaller than a grain of barley,
smaller than a mustard seed,
smaller than a grain of millet.

God is the soul within my heart
– greater than the earth,
greater than the sky,
greater than the heavens,
greater than all the worlds.

God is the soul within my heart.

(from the Chandogya Upanishad, *c*.400 BCE)

The Great Night of Shiva (Maha-shiva-ratri)

13th of the month of Magha
February/March

Most Hindus worship either Vishnu in one of his forms, or Shiva. Together with Brahma they make up the Supreme Trinity of gods encompassing all others. They themselves are aspects of the One God who is so vast and incomprehensible that we must pass through various levels, or stages, of understanding before his nature can be fully comprehended. Most Hindus join together to celebrate many different gods while maintaining their particular devotion for one – usually Vishnu or Shiva. Yogis, however, attempt to realise their understanding of their own inner being which, once found, becomes a unity with the true God.

Brahma, Vishnu, and Shiva are generally understood to be three natures of one God – the creator, the maintainer, and the destroyer of the universe respectively. Creation revolves in cycles: just as a flower grows and dies, yet leaves its seed to grow again, so it is with the material universe, with human and other life, with planets, stars and galaxies. Shiva is responsible for the destruction which must precede new growth. He is a paradox, for he also represents fertility and is depicted with his mount, the bull Nandi, and symbolised by a smooth round pillar of stone, originally a phallic symbol. Shiva is also called Nata-raja, the King of Dance, who takes his followers with him on the joyful dance of life in its destruction of illusion and consequent knowledge of the cyclic nature of all things. Formerly a storm deity Shiva carries a trident representing lightning. He is shown with the tangled hair of an ascetic yogi and is held to be the lord and master of such people and high priest of the gods.

Shiva-ratri is a solemn remembrance of the god during which devotees fast (sometimes abstaining from food and water for thirty-six hours) and Shiva's exploits are remembered in verse and song through the night. Hermits, monks, yogis, and ascetics hold this as their special day but everyone joins in with song and especially with dance to praise the Great Yogi.

Shiva, Lord of Dance   (2 min.)

Shiva-ratri is a festival for Shiva, one of India's three great gods. Hindus call God by the name Brahma when he created the universe; they call him Vishnu as he looks after it; and they call him Shiva when he destroys it ready to start all over again. When Hindus think of God as Shiva, they think of him as a very powerful god.

There is a legend that tells of the time when Shiva appeared to ten thousand hermits. These hermits lived away from everyone else, but they did not believe in the truth. When Shiva arrived they swore at him and gave him no welcome at all. Shiva explained that he came among them to be a priest so that they could learn the truth, but they were ruder still. As Shiva spoke to them, the hermits released a terrible tiger upon the god. The tiger was nothing to Shiva. As it leaped to attack him, Shiva put out his little finger. The tiger sprang, and Shiva split its skin from its body, threw down the carcass, and draped the tiger skin over his back like a cloak.

The hermits let out a great snake. As it slid towards Shiva hissing and showing its poisonous fangs, Shiva reached down and wrapped it around him like a garland of flowers.

The hermits were rather worried by now, and they set loose their nastiest weapon. This was a demon dwarf with jet black skin and black clothes, who charged towards Shiva with an enormous club. Shiva lifted his foot, pushing the evil dwarf to the ground, began to dance on the dwarf's back. He danced as only the Lord of Dance can. The hermits watched in amazement, hypnotised by the skill and rhythm of Shiva's dance. Then the heavens opened and the hermits could see the other gods watching Shiva. The hermits fell on their knees in worship. Shiva had opened their eyes to the truth.

The Churning of the Ocean   (3 min.)

Shiva is the protector of gods and men. Now there was once a time when the power and the force of the gods began to slow down and grow weak. With them, the forces that drive the world also began to fade. One of the three Great Gods, Vishnu, knew what to do. Just as milk can be churned to make butter, Vishnu told the other gods, so the sea could be churned to make a special drink which would bring everything to life and give the gods back their strength and power for ever.

Vishnu made a secret mixture of herbs which he threw into the sea. Then he asked the demons, normally the enemies of the gods, to help. The gods made a bargain with the demons to let them share some of their special drink, amritsar, if they would help to churn up the seas.

Gods and demons searched for a rope big enough to pull back and forth across the sea to churn it. They found that no rope was long enough or strong enough. Finally they seized a gigantic sea serpent, Vasuki, wrapped his long body twice around Mount Mandara, and began to heave backwards and forwards across the waters. Attached to the great swinging serpent, the mountain slowly ground round this way, then the other, and it began to bore down into the earth, threatening to break right through.

Vishnu immediately turned himself into a giant turtle and thrust himself underneath the root of the mountain. The churning went on getting faster by the minute. The snake, Vasuki, began to spew out torrents of poisonous venom from his fangs. As Shiva heaved on the gods' end of the serpent, he realised that the poison was going to land in the sea killing gods and men alike. He let go of the snake's tail and dived towards the falling poison and caught it in his mouth before any fell into the ocean. Shiva's wife realised what he was doing and rushed over to help. Before he could swallow the poison which she knew would kill him, she put her hands tightly round his throat. He was nearly strangled and his throat turned bright blue with the poison inside it, but the god was saved. And so was the power of the gods for the churning of the sea had produced the life-giving drink they needed.

Shiva's Third Eye   (1 min.)

Statues and paintings of Shiva show him with a third eye in the middle of his forehead. His wife, Parvati, sneaked up behind him, in the days when he had only two eyes, and playfully put her hands over them so he could not see who it was. As she covered the god's eyes, the sun went out and the earth plunged into a cold and silent darkness. Plants and animals began to die. From Shiva's forehead grew a third eye of burning light and warmth which gave life to the world once more.

*

A Hindu morning prayer:

  O Lord, hear my call:
  I cry to you longing for help;

Be good to us this day.
O wise God, you are Lord of all,
You are King of heaven and earth;
Hear my prayer.

(from the Vedas, *c*.1500 BCE)

Shiva and Parvati   (2 min.)

Parvati wanted to win Shiva for her husband but he was always at prayer and meditation. He never even noticed her. Day after day she waited patiently at his side, but Shiva was lost in thought. The other gods took pity on Parvati and sent Kama, the god of love and Kama's wife, Pleasure, to warm the great Shiva's heart.

As Parvati went to Shiva one day, Kama hid nearby. Parvati went to where Shiva sat cross-legged in meditation. Kama pulled back his bow to shoot an arrow of love at Shiva. At that very moment the great god looked up. With the burning power of Shiva's third eye Kama was burned up in a second. Pleasure wept for her husband, when a voice boomed, echoing across the heavens, 'When Parvati and Shiva come together, Pleasure will have her husband once more.'

In the meantime Parvati, despairing of ever having Shiva for herself, had gone off into the hills to live the life of a hermit. One day a young priest visited her and said how much he admired her faithfulness to Shiva. After all, she could have found herself another husband from among the gods by now. But he asked her if she would come back to the world for she was greatly missed. Parvati grew angry when she thought how Shiva had ignored her and she refused. But when the priest revealed that he was actually Shiva himself, her heart softened. She agreed on one condition: that Pleasure should be given back her husband, Kama. Shiva gladly agreed and both he and Parvati, and Kama and Pleasure were united.

Bell-ears   (2 min.)

The stories of Shiva help people to understand what God is like and how they should behave. They believe that God is so big that it is difficult to understand him without such help.

There is a story of a man called Bell-ears. He was called Bell-ears because he wore ear-rings which tinkled like bells. Bell-ears worshipped the god Shiva. He worshipped him so much and so often that he refused to hear any other god's name mentioned, let alone celebrate his festival. Whenever anyone was heard praying to a different god, Bell-ears would shake his head and make the bells ring in his ears. In this way the tinkling bells would drown the noise of the other god's praise so Bell-ears could not hear it.

God grew tired of this silly performance by Bell-ears and decided that he would show him that he was not just Shiva nor was he just any other god but that he was all the gods together, and greater than all of them.

One day, when Bell-ears worshipped at the foot of Shiva's statue in the temple, he suddenly noticed that the statue had changed. One half of it was Shiva, but the other half had changed into Vishnu. God wanted to show Bell-ears that he is Shiva, that he is Vishnu, that he is all the gods. But Bell-ears still refused to understand. He lit the sweet-smelling incense sticks, he sang his songs of praise and he burned candles before the statue. And he put his hands over the eyes, ears and nose of the Vishnu side of the statue so that Vishnu could not see, hear or smell the praise he wanted to give to Shiva.

A true worshipper of Shiva wrote:

> God taught me the way of holy love
> As I worked away in a world of fools
> Who didn't know the way to peace.
> He rid me of my selfish ways,
> Made me pure bliss
> And took me for his own.
> How blessed I am that the Father gave me grace.

(from a prayer by Manikka Vasagar, 9th century BCE)

Three Gods are One   (1 min.)

Once, during the time between the end of the old universe and before the new one had been created, Brahma and Vishnu and Shiva met each other in the silent still darkness. Shiva spoke for all three:

'I am the highest Lord. I cannot be split up. I am one and I am three – Brahma, Vishnu and Shiva: as Brahma I create the universe, as Vishnu I look after it, and as Shiva I destroy it.'

The Hunter in the Tree   (3 min.)

Mahashivaratri is Shiva's great festival. It is a special time for monks and hermits, for they hold Shiva to be their own special god. Some people fast for thirty-six hours in Shiva's honour. The day after Shiva's Night, fairs are held and there is great rejoicing.

This legend tells why people fast on Shiva's Night. One day a hunter was chasing a tiger. The tiger turned on him and the hunter scrambled up a tree to safety. The tree was a vilwa tree, Shiva's sacred tree, and it happened to be growing near to a small shrine with a statue of Shiva in it. The tiger prowled back and forth at the foot of the tree and the hunter had to stay put. As night fell the tiger lay down and still the hunter had to stay where he was. He could feel his eyes getting heavy and his mind getting sleepy. He had to keep himself awake for he knew that if he fell asleep, he would fall out of the tree; and the tiger would surely kill him. So to keep himself awake, the hunter patiently, one by one, plucked the leaves from the tree, dropped them and watched them float down in the moonlight to land on the shrine of Shiva below. Shiva felt that he was being worshipped and by morning the tiger had gone and the hunter climbed down the bare tree to safety. The hunter had nothing to eat until the tiger left, so nowadays worshippers of Shiva also practise patient fasting in honour of their god because they believe that is how he likes to be praised.

*

At the end of the festival of Mahashivaratri, Hindus will say this prayer as they do at the end of all ceremonies. The word 'Aum' is a sacred word to a Hindu. It means 'God Most High'. Prayers usually start and finish with the 'Aum'.

Aum.

Peace be in the heavens,
Peace be in the depths,
Peace be on the earth.

May the waters flow peacefully,
May the herbs and shrubs grow peacefully,
May all the powers of the gods bring us to peace.

May all be in peace,
In peace, and only in peace,
And may that peace come also to me.

Aum.
Peace. Peace. Peace.

(from a traditional Hindu devotional prayer)

The Festival of Colour (Holi)

Full-moon day of the month of Phalgun
late February/March

The five-day festival of Holi marks the beginning of the spring wheat harvest in India. The festival originated with the death of Holika in a fire meant to kill Prahlada, a great devotee of the god Vishnu. In the story Vishnu appears in his fourth incarnation as a man-lion to kill the demon Hiranyakasipu and maintain the balance between good and evil. Holi is now linked with the story of Krishna and the village girls. Krishna, the eighth incarnation of Vishnu, was born at Mathura, Uttar Pradesh, between Delhi and Agra. The story of Krishna's youth is the story of his many loves. These symbolise the union of man and God. In Indian towns and villages great images of Krishna and his consort Radha are wheeled through the streets, while coloured water and powder is joyfully thrown on to the participants. In some parts effigies of the demoness Putana are burned celebrating the child Krishna's victory over her. Plays about Krishna's life are performed. These concentrate especially on the god's adolescent flirtations with the village girls. (See also the Birthday of Krishna.)

*

Prahlada and Holika   (5 min.)

Hiranyakasipu was a powerful but evil king whose only thoughts were for himself. Everything he did was selfish. But Hiranyakasipu was not satisfied. He wanted to be stronger than all men – that was easy; but he wanted to be stronger than the gods themselves. He sent out a decree all around his kingdom that from that day forth there would be no worship of the gods in the temples, no more sacrifices to the gods at the altars, no hymns to the gods at festivals and no more prayers to the gods in people's houses in the mornings. Instead the people must worship him. They were to pray, to sing, and to sacrifice to Hiranyakasipu. The people were so afraid of their evil King that they could do nothing but obey.

However, Hiranyakasipu had a son called Prahlada. Prahlada was a worshipper of the great god Vishnu – it would need more than his father's decree to stop him worshipping his god. When Prahlada got up in the morning at the palace of Hiranyakasipu, he opened the window and sang his hymn of praise to Vishnu. Everything in the palace stopped, shocked into silence. What would the King do? The gardeners stopped weeding, the cooks stopped making the breakfast, the servants all stood still and listened – and

King Hiranyakasipu stopped sleeping. As his eyes slowly opened and he began to wake up, he could hear the song of praise to Vishnu.

He ordered the guards to bring the singer to him at once.

Imagine the fury of the King when the soldiers brought before him his own son, Prahlada.

'In this country there is no-one greater than me,' he stormed. 'Now get down on your knees and sing your praises to me!'

'You are a strong king, Father,' replied Prahlada. 'But I worship only God. I shall sing to Vishnu.'

Hiranyakasipu nearly exploded with anger. He had Prahlada taken to the dungeons and tortured. He had him beaten. At last he threw him out on to the streets. But it seemed that his father's cruelty had made Prahlada's faith stronger and he went round preaching about Vishnu.

Hiranyakasipu angrily made various plots against his son but all of them failed. He began to think that perhaps Vishnu was protecting his son. Finally he had Prahlada arrested and brought back to the palace. Hiranyakasipu had another plan to get rid of Prahlada.

He suspected that the people he had entrusted to kill Prahlada were really on Prahlada's side. The only person Hiranyakasipu could rely on was his sister, Holika. She put on a fireproof cloak and tricked Prahlada into sitting with her on top of a pile of wood. As they sat there the wood was lit beneath them and the flames leaped up towards them. The fire burned so fiercely and with such heat that even the fireproof cloak that Holika was wearing was no protection. She burned to death in the flames. But once again Vishnu looked after his faithful follower and Prahlada stepped off the blazing fire unhurt.

Hiranyakasipu once more took Prahlada prisoner. Prahlada was brought before Hiranyakasipu who sat on his throne and laughed at his son

'Your faith in Vishnu is like an empty jug,' said the King. 'Only bow down and worship me and I shall set you free and call you my son again. After all; what's the use of a god that you can't even see?'

'God is everywhere whether you can see him or not,' answered Prahlada calmly.

'Rubbish,' replied the king. 'Do you mean to say that he's in this palace, in this room? If I hit this stone pillar, do you mean he's in there too?'

Hiranyakasipu hit angrily at one of the pillars with his sword and swore at the god Vishnu:

'If God's in there, let him come and save you then!' he called.

As Hiranyakasipu spoke these evil words, Vishnu turned the pillar of stone into a fierce creature with the body of a man and the head of a lion. The man-lion was Vishnu himself. Hiranyakasipu turned pale and screamed with terror. It was the last thing he ever did, for in seconds the lion-god had torn the wicked king to pieces.

So Vishnu showed himself as God in all his glory to the people of the court, and they bowed down to worship with Prahlada, who had always had faith in God.

*

This is a well-known Hindu prayer:

We praise you with our thoughts, O God;
We praise you as the sun praises you in the morning:
May we find joy in being your servants;
Keep us in your care,
Forgive us our sins,
And give us your love.

(from the Rig Veda, c.1500 BCE)

Lord Krishna and the Priests' Wives   (2 min.)

Krishna was born in India many years ago, at a time when a cruel and wicked king ruled the land. Krishna was, in fact, the great god Vishnu who had come to earth as a human being to help fight against evil. Throughout his childhood Krishna had shown that he was no ordinary person. He had defeated wickedness even when very young, and he was the friend of all people who searched for goodness.

Krishna was walking with his friends one day as he was growing to manhood. They had worked hard and played hard and were feeling hungry when they smelled the delicious scent of cooking food. They followed their noses and found themselves at a temple where the priests were busily cooking. Krishna asked if they could have something to eat.

Not knowing who Krishna was, the priests angrily told him that they were preparing the food as an offering for the gods and he couldn't have any. The priests' wives had been listening, however. They went home and brought Krishna and his friends plenty to eat. They had seen in Krishna's eyes that he was no ordinary youth. Krishna and his friends thanked them and left.

When the priests went home and found out what their wives had done, they were not angry. Indeed, they forgave them and said how sorry they were that they had turned the young god away from their temple.

*

However many sins a man has committed in his lifetime, just let him love me with a true heart and in true faith, and I shall see no sinner before me but a holy man.

(from the Bhagavad Gita, c.1st century CE)

Krishna and the Village Girls   (2 min.)

Because Krishna was God born on earth, it was only natural that everyone who met him should feel that he was a very special person. Children felt that Krishna would be a perfect father to them. Men felt that he was a perfect friend and soldiers felt that he was the perfect officer. Parents felt that he was the perfect child, and women felt that he would make the perfect husband. Everyone saw something special in him. There are many stories of Krishna causing the girls to fall in love with him; Krishna was a god in the form of a man and enjoyed teasing them.

One autumn night Krishna went into the forest. He sat down in the moonlight to play his flute. The girls from the village heard its magical notes and all left their houses to join him. Krishna began to dance with them. As the girls danced, each one thought she was dancing with Krishna. The dance went on getting faster and more excited, when the girls suddenly realised they were alone. Krishna had gone.

Then one of the girls found Krishna's footprints. He had gone deeper into the forest. Quickly the girls followed the footprints. They came upon Radha, one of their friends, and her eyes were filled with tears. Krishna had asked Radha to go with him, which she had done. As they went further Radha began to feel so proud that Krishna had chosen her that she had asked Krishna to carry her. Krishna was so annoyed that he left her on the spot. Now she was in tears and Krishna had gone.

The girls hunted and called out and searched and shouted until at last Krishna decided they should be forgiven and joined them in the dance again. This time the dancing was wilder and even more excited than before. Though Krishna danced only with Radha, again each girl thought that he danced with her. It seemed that the dance had lasted for six months, but when they all returned home, their parents didn't even know they'd been out.

Krishna Kills the Demon Kansa   (7 min.)

Krishna had now grown to manhood. It was time for him to do what the gods had asked. On earth was a wicked king called Kansa. It was believed that he was a demon who ruled selfishly and with great cruelty. Evil was the only thing that Kansa knew. Krishna's task was to overcome Kansa's wickedness.

Hearing of Krishna, he was filled with hate and attempted to kill him a number of times. Kansa sent one of his men to attack Krishna and his friends while they talked with the village girls. But Krishna chased after the murderer and cut off his head. Kansa arranged that a mad bull charged from among the herd of cattle which Krishna was looking after one night, but Krishna seized it as it lunged at him and broke its neck. Several times Kansa's nasty schemes failed because Krishna was too strong to be beaten.

Kansa decided to change his plans. If brute force was no good, he would have to try and trick Krishna. He invited Krishna to a feast in honour of the god Shiva. But the messenger Kansa sent was a secret friend of Krishna's. He warned him that a trap was to be set for him when he arrived at Kansa's palace. The trap was this. Krishna was to be challenged to a wrestling match by one of the country's greatest wrestlers. However, the wrestler was not going to fight fairly. He would kill Krishna when he got the chance. If that plan failed Kansa had arranged for a savage elephant to trample him to death if he tried to escape.

Everyone in the village tried to persuade Krishna not to trust Kansa. They knew that Krishna was a very special person, and they knew that the wicked Kansa would stop at nothing to get his own way. But Krishna set off for the town. The news that he was coming travelled quickly and Krishna was welcomed like a king. People crowded the streets, waved from their windows and even climbed up on to the rooftops to watch him pass by. In his palace Kansa was jealous. He seethed with anger but his plan was ready.

As Krishna came towards the palace, Kansa was told that his own tailor had made Krishna a new suit of clothes. Kansa, bursting with fury, could wait no longer. He screamed from the windows for his guards to attack Krishna. But Krishna and his friends killed most of them and chased away the rest.

As Krishna marched through the gates of the palace, the wild elephant snapped the great chains that fastened it to the gatepost and thundered towards Krishna and his friends. His friends scattered but Krishna stood and faced the charging animal. He threw himself at the elephant, grasping its head. The elephant screamed, shaking its head madly from side to side. But Krishna's strength was greater. He knew that he had to defeat the evil of Kansa at all costs. With a shudder that shook the palace Krishna brought the elephant to the ground and held it long enough to stab his sword deep into its heart.

Now Kansa sent out his wrestlers to attack the tired Krishna. The mightiest of them attacked first followed by many more. But one by one Krishna and his friends defeated them and they lay injured and unable to move or else ran away too quickly to be caught.

There now seemed to be nothing to stop Krishna from ridding the world of the evil Kansa. But as Krishna entered the throne room of the palace, he found that Kansa was not alone. Held by his guards were three people.

Kansa shouted out, 'Come no further. I have some prisoners here you might like to meet. First, the king upon whose throne I sit.'

Everyone was amazed. It has been thought that the real king of the country had been put to death when Kansa had taken over. But here he was, weak and old, but still alive.

Kansa went on, 'And secondly, your mother and father.'

Again there was astonishment. Krishna had been brought up by foster parents. His real mother and father had been unknown. Now they were the prisoners of Kansa.

'I shall kill you and your parents together,' hissed Kansa.

But Kansa did not expect what happened next. Before he had time to carry out his threat, Krishna had rushed at the guards, slashing with his sword. He came to where the evil Kansa stood and without a pause stabbed him through the heart. He had done this in less time than it takes to blink an eye.

Everyone was so amazed and relieved that no one spoke for several moments. Then cheering and singing and shouting were heard. There was joy in the streets outside the palace when the news of Kansa's death reached the people of the town. Krishna had found his parents and the real king could rule once more.

Once again peace and freedom could be enjoyed by everyone.

*

In the Song of the Lord about the life of Krishna, the god says:

God is the light of lights
and brighter
than all the darkness of our ignorance.
(from the Bhagavad Gita, c.1st century CE).

Rama's Birthday (Rama Navami)

9th of the month of Chaitra
March/April

One of the ten earthly descents of Vishnu, the second Hindu Trinity, is Rama, the seventh incarnation. Vishnu appears as Rama in order to redress the balance between good and evil in his role as preserver of the world. Specifically Rama's job was to destroy the power of the ten-headed demon king, Ravana of Lanka (formerly known as Ceylon). His exploits are recorded in the great epic poem, the 'Ramayana' which was first written down about the 5th century BCE. Rama was the king of Ayodhya, roughly corresponding to the modern state of Uttar Pradesh where the festival is especially celebrated. He and his wife, Sita (who is an incarnation of Vishnu's consort, Lakshmi) are held up as examples of ideal virtue to Indian children today. (See The Ten Days for the conclusion of this story.)

Rama and Sita Leave the Kingdom   (6 min.)

Rama is God on earth. When it looked as if evil would overcome the world, the gods sent down Vishnu, one of the Three Great Gods, to be born a human being. He was born as Rama, the son of the King of Ayodhya in northern India. The story of Rama is one in which terrible wrongs are committed, great mistakes are made, but in which bravery and steadfastness and truth conquer evil in the end.

The old King of Ayodhya was particularly proud of his eldest son, Rama, and looked forward to the day when he would retire and allow Rama to become king in his place. There was great joy and celebrations when Rama announced that he intended to ask for the hand of the beautiful princess, Sita. Sita's father owned the great bow of the god, Shiva. He proclaimed that any man who could bend the bow could take the hand of his daughter in marriage.

The contest was held at the palace of Sita's father. Crowds came to watch as princes and noblemen from all the kingdoms of India used every ounce of strength to pull at the enormous bow. But not one could bend it by even a millimetre. Some couldn't even lift it at all! Rama's turn came. He lifted the great bow, and began to pull. It didn't move. Harder he pulled until at last, with a sudden great crack, the bow split and snapped. Soon afterwards Rama and Sita were married.

There was great happiness at the court of the King of Ayodhya. There was even greater rejoicing when the old king announced that he had decided to retire and hand over the throne to his son, Rama. All Rama's brothers loved him – there was no jealousy among them at all. They were glad Rama was to be king.

But not everyone in the palace was happy. One of the king of Ayodhya's wives believed that her son, Bharata, would be imprisoned and that she would be made a slave if ever Rama came to be king. Bharata was away in another country so the wife went to Ayodhya and said,'Do you remember that you granted me two wishes some time ago?'

'Yes, wife, I do,' replied Ayodhya. 'Only ask for what you want and I shall give it to you.'

'Then I ask that you crown our son, Bharata, as king, and send Rama into the forest for fourteen years.'

The old king's heart sank. He was filled with grief as soon as he saw what he had done in one careless moment. But he had made a promise and he was a man of his word. He declared that Bharata would be king and Rama was banished to the great forest.

When Bharata came back he found his brother Rama had gone and his father had died of a broken heart. He was furious with his mother. He told her he would never be king for he had no right. Instead he would go and find Rama and bring him back.

The ministers of the court told him, 'You must stay here as king. You cannot disobey your father's wishes.'

But Bharata would not listen. He rushed out of the city and caught up with Rama on his way to the forest. He begged Rama to come back and take the throne that should be his, but Rama told Bharata he must do his duty whether it was pleasant or not.

'Go back and rule the land wisely,' said Rama as they sadly waved goodbye to each other.

When Bharata came back to the palace, he told the people that he would not be crowned king. Rama was the rightful king. Bharata placed a pair of Rama's shoes on the royal throne to remind him that he was only going to rule for fourteen years in Rama's place until Rama came back to claim the throne for himself.

Bharata was not the only one who followed Rama on the track into the forest. The princess Sita begged Rama to take her with him.

'No, Sita,' said Rama. 'The journey will be dangerous and the life is far too rough for the gentle daughter of a king. The forest is full of the roaring of lions and the thunder of waterfalls. There will be times when there is not enough to drink, fallen fruit will be your only food, snakes will slide silently across the path, and the hard earth will be your only resting place. You must stay in the comfort of the palace and leave me to face the land of winds and darkness, of hunger and terror on my own.'

But Sita was not to be put off by Rama's words. 'If it is your duty to leave the kingdom, it is my duty as your wife to go with you. Whether it will be heaven or hell, I will go with you.'

Together Rama and Sita set out to face the unknown dangers of the forest.

*

Rama did what he thought was his duty – and so did his brother and his father. A Hindu book of law says that you should do what is right, because you know it is right, and not just to get yourself a place in heaven:

Learn that sacred law which is followed by all those who know the Holy

Books, the law which is followed in their hearts by all who are good and free from hate:

To be good only in the hope of being rewarded
Is not to be good at all.

(from the Laws of Manu, *c.*200 CE)

The Day of Snakes (Naga Panchami)

5th of the month of Shravan
July/August

Snakes are commonly found in India, including such deadly poisonous species as the cobra. They are regarded ambivalently and worshipped as gods for protection against their attack as much as anything. In southern India snake temples and shrines are placed in uncultivated ground, whether in public places or in a private garden, the belief being that if they have their own area, they will not attack human beings. Snakes in general are called 'nagas'. Their king is Takshaka who has the power to appear in many forms, and the snake gods are Shesha (or Ananta) the divine friend of Vishnu on whom the god rests in the period between the destruction and creation of the universe, and Manasa, the Bengali goddess particularly worshipped at this festival. Manasa is sometimes referred to as a daughter of Shiva, one of the Supreme Trinity, or as an aspect of Shiva's wife.

The Snake-goddess Chooses her First Worshipper   (11 min.)

Manasa is the Hindu snake-goddess. She is worshipped especially in Bengal for her power. People pray to her for protection against snakebites, for there are many very dangerous snakes in India. There was a time when nobody worshipped this goddess and this is the story of how Manasa chose a man of very strong character to be her first worshipper.

Manasa chose a man named Chand to be her first worshipper. Chand was a rich and hard-working merchant whose pride and joy was his garden. Every spare minute he had he would spend walking in the garden, smelling the flowers, watching the leaves of the trees rustling in the breeze, pulling up the tiniest weeds before they had chance to grow. He loved his garden. Unlike the servants of other rich men, Chand's servants did not spend much time in the house; they spent their time looking after the garden and were almost as proud of it as Chand was himself.

As Chand sat in his beautiful garden one day, a snake slid across the flower bed and towards the seat where he sat. Chand did not move. He sat quite still. But the snake came across the path straight for him. When the snake coiled itself round at Chand's feet and raised its head and flickered its tongue, Chand sat as still as a statue with fear.

'I am Manasa the Snake-Goddess,' hissed the snake. 'Bow down before me and worship me.'

As Chand sat there frozen with fright, he thought that the goddess was simply using her power to make him worship her. Dangerous or not, he would not worship any god out of fear.

He had hardly finished saying the word 'No' when he saw his beautiful garden destroyed. It happened in a second. The trees had lost their leaves, flowers were dead, plants were brown and withered. The paths were cracked and filled with weeds, statues were broken and the streams ran dry. The garden that had taken Chand so long to build up, that he loved so much, was in ruins.

Even a rich man cannot have a garden rebuilt and filled with beautiful plants in days, weeks, or months. Chand worked for several years to get his garden back to what it was. He spent thousands of rupees and hours and hours of his own time until his garden was once more as magnificent as ever.

As Chand sat in the cool of the evening enjoying the sights and smells a beautiful woman walked into the garden. She said she was a worshipper of the goddess Manasa and asked Chand if he would get down on his knees and pray with her to the mighty goddess of snakes. Chand realised who it was had entered his garden. He thought about the trouble he had brought on himself last time he had refused to worship her. But once again he said 'No'.

Years of hard work were gone in seconds. Chand sat and wept as he looked at his ruined garden.

But Manasa had not finished. She was testing Chand for his strength of character. She did not want a worshipper who would change his mind when he grew bored. She wanted a strong man who would stick to his beliefs through thick and thin. She decided to put Chand's strength of character to an even greater test.

Chand had six sons. One by one during the next months they were brought home with the two small fang marks of the deadly cobra on their bodies. One by one all six died of the poison.

Some time later Chand went off with his fleet of merchant ships to do business abroad. On the way a storm blew up and every ship was wrecked. It was a miracle that Chand was washed ashore clinging to a plank. But he was a ruined man. He had lost all his sons. He had lost all his money and he was many many miles from home.

It was a slow difficult journey back. Chand had to walk all the way. He had no money for food. Several times Manasa appeared to him and promised to help him if he would worship her, but each time Chand refused. After months of hard travel Chand reached his home. He settled down with his wife to try to start again. Soon a new son was born, a boy they called Lakshmindra. As the years went by and Lakshmindra grew up, he became engaged to a girl called Behula. It came to Chand in a dream that his son would die of a snake-bite on the very first night of his marriage to Behula. Chand woke up, cold but sweating. He sat there in the darkness and planned what he would do to save his son.

As the marriage day drew nearer, Chand's workmen were busy. Chand hired a famous architect to build him a house made entirely of metal and completely snake-proof. The house was finished in time for the wedding and Chand was very pleased. But there was something that he did not know. The famous architect had also met the snake-goddess. She had threatened to kill his family one by one if he did not leave a place in the metal house where a snake could slip in. What could the poor man do? And so when the metal house was finished, out of sight, round the back, near the ground was a small gap in the wall.

Lakshmindra and Behula were married. The wedding party went on through the day and well into the night; but at last it was time for the bride and bridegroom to go back to their new home together. Tired and happy Lakshmindra went to bed with the door locked safely behind him. It did not take him long to fall into a deep sleep after such a long day.

Suddenly, in the darkness of the night, Behula heard a soft sound. Lakshmindra was still fast asleep. She lit a light to see a snake sliding across the floor of their bedroom. Thinking quickly she put her night-time cup of milk on the floor by the bed. The snake slid over to the cup and began to drink. As quick as a flash Behula grabbed the snake's neck and held it tightly.

With her handkerchief she tied the snake to the leg of the bed – and Lakshmindra slept on. But as she finished tying the knot, another snake appeared, which she dealt with in the same way. But then another and another. Behula grew tired and eventually she could keep her eyes open no longer. As she fell asleep, another snake came into the room, across the floor, up on to the bed, over the sleeping Behula and up to Lakshmindra. When morning came Behula awoke to find that her husband was dead with two small fang marks on his body.

Chand realised what had happened. Sadly the family laid Lakshmindra's body on to a raft. It was said that life remains in a body for some time after a snake-bite and it was hoped that floating it down the holy river might by some miracle bring it back to life. As they pushed the raft out into the water, Behula could not bear to see it go. She jumped into the river and climbed on to the raft with her husband.

Days and months passed and still Behula floated downstream with her dead husband. Nothing the priests said to her from the river banks as the raft drifted by made any difference. Magicians from the villages gave advice, but Lakshmindra still remained dead.

One day the raft stopped by the bank where a washerwoman was beating and scrubbing clothes to get them clean. Her little son kept making the woman cross until at last she could bear it no more. She hit out at the boy and struck him on the head. She hit him so hard that she killed him. But she was not upset. She dipped her hand into the water and sprinkled some over the boy. Then she said some kind of spell and before long he rubbed his eyes and got up again. Almost weeping with joy, Behula rushed up to the old lady and asked if she would do the same for Lakshmindra.

'I am Manasa the washerwoman,' said the old lady. 'I may be able to help you. But tell me this. Are you and your family worshippers of the great Snake-Goddess?'

'Well, no,' answered Behula.

'Not your husband, nor your father-in-law, Chand?'

'No, they're not.'

'Well, unless you can make them all worshippers of the Snake-Goddess, I cannot help you. The very second that your husband's father bows down to worship, your husband will be brought back to life.'

Behula returned to Chand's house again as quickly as she could. She told Chand all that had happened. Chand could bear it no longer. He had been as strong as any man could be, but his strength was used up. Without another word he walked into the garden where he asked one of the gardeners to bring him a snake and place it under a tree. Chand knelt down and said, 'O mighty Snake-Goddess, Manasa, I, your humble servant Chand, bow down before you. I beg you to give back the life of my son, Lakshmindra.'

As he finished speaking Lakshmindra walked from the house into the garden. Father and son were filled with joy.

So it was that Chand became the first man to worship Manasa, the goddess of snakes.

*

To a Hindu, God appears in many different forms. This prayer is actually addressed to Rama and asks God to give the worshipper the strength to be faithful to God:

O God, give me faith, devotion and love
So I always may sing your holy name.

Let my heart overflow with your love
And let me realise the glory of your name.
Let me live in you; and awaken my soul
That your light will forever shine in my life.

(from the writings of Dadu, *c*.17th century CE)

Coconut Day (Narali Purnima)
and
The Ties of Protection (Raksha Bandhan or Rakhi Purnima)

Full-moon day of the month of Shravan
July/August

Two festivals take place on this day. Narali Purnima marks the end of the monsoon season in India. Hindus throw coconuts into rivers, into lakes, and into the sea. They do this to commemorate Varuna, god of the sea and former god of the rain. The coconut itself, however, is considered to be Shiva's fruit, its three eyes corresponding to the three eyes of the third of the Supreme Trinity.

Rakhi Purnima or Raksha Bandhan celebrates the occasion when Indra, king of the lesser gods (those inferior to the Supreme Trinity) was beaten by the demon, Bali. Indrani, Indra's wife asked Vishnu, second of the Trinity for help, and was given a thread to tie around her husband's wrist. This protected Indra and gave him the power to defeat the evil demon.

The modern Raksha Bandhan ceremony originated in the 17th century CE as a reaction to Mughal atrocities on Hindu women. A band (raksha) made of multicoloured threads is tied by a sister on the right hand of her own, or adopted brother who is then obliged to protect the sister at all times. The rite involves brother and sister covering their heads while the raksha is tied. The sister paints a red mark on the brother's forehead and gives him a sweet. The brother presents her with a gift.

Those Hindus who wear the triple-stranded sacred thread renew these on this day. The thread is placed over a boy's shoulders from the left shoulder, at about the age of twelve, but when he becomes married a man wears it across the right shoulder. Its triple nature is deeply symbolic of many things in Hindu belief: it reminds the wearer of the triune nature of God as we understand him, being Brahma, Vishnu and Shiva; of the cyclical nature of the universe, being created, existing and being destroyed; and of the three-fold nature of man, being soul, mind and body. At this ceremony, as at all Hindu ceremonies, the Gayatri Mantra is repeated with its triple Sanskrit rhythm three times. In it God is referred to as Savitri, the God of the Rising Sun, the symbol of the life-giving nature of God. It is normally also said three times a day – at dawn, at noon, and at sunset:

Let us think on the glorious splendour of God (Savitri) that he will fill our minds with understanding.

Real Sisterly Love   (3 min.)

The festival of Raksha Bandhan is a time when Hindu brothers and sisters think of the care they must show to one another. This is the story of a faithful sister.

About five thousand years ago the god Vishnu was born on earth as an ordinary human baby. His parents called him Krishna. Krishna is one of the best-loved Hindu gods nowadays, but he was just as much loved when he was alive. However, there are different kinds of love – there is love which is shallow and disappears as soon as hardships or difficulties come along – that is false love; and there is love that is deep and lasts through all kinds of dangers – that is real love.

Krishna had two sisters. One was his real sister called Subhadra, and the other was an adopted sister by the name of Draupadi. Subhadra was always complaining and grumbling about Draupadi. She was jealous.

One day she said to Krishna, 'You are my *real* brother. Draupadi is only an adopted sister. You should love me best of all, Krishna.'

'If I love Draupadi more than I love you, perhaps it is because she loves me more than you do,' answered Krishna.

'That's rubbish,' said Subhadra. 'You know I would do anything for you.'

Not long after this it happened that Krishna cut his hand rather badly. The cut was deep and it bled quite a lot. Krishna came in and asked Subhadra to look at it.

'It's a bad cut,' she said, 'but there's nothing I can do. I'll go and see if I can find a bandage for you.'

Subhadra went out of the door and was gone for rather a long time. Meanwhile, Krishna's hand was still pouring with blood. Draupadi came in. As soon as she saw her adopted brother's hand she tore a strip from the sari she was wearing and wrapped it around the wound. Gradually the bleeding stopped. Subhadra never did come back with the bandage.

Subhadra was Krishna's real sister. Draupadi was adopted. Which sister had real love for her brother though?

*

Show love to all and you will be happy;
For when you love all, you love God,
For God is in all things.

(from the Ramayana of Tulsi Das, 5th century BCE)

Savitri, a Faithful Wife   (9 min.)

Savitri was the only daughter of an Indian king. As she grew to be a woman she became more and more beautiful. She was so beautiful and good that stories of the princess went around the country. All the sons of nobles and princes wanted to marry her, but none dared ask.

The king her father began to worry. If no one would come to ask for Savitri's hand in marriage, he would have to send her off to find someone herself. And so for many months Savitri travelled round from palace to palace but still she found no one she wanted to marry. She met many handsome princes, but most of them were selfish and insincere. They said how they cared for their country, but as Savitri went through from city to city she came across people who were hungry and poor. She saw that, for all their fine words, the princes cared nothing for the poor and the hungry people. Sadly Savitri travelled on in the hope that she would one day find a prince who cared for others just as she did. But she found no one.

At last Savitri returned home. On the way she came to a forest. There she found a hermitage – a place of peace and quiet where people would stay to think. Savitri felt that she needed time to think. When she came to the hermitage, she found that somebody was already there. It was an old blind king who had been forced out of his kingdom to live in the forest, poor and unknown. With him was his son, Satyavan.

Although they had nothing that compared with the rich kings and princes in their wonderful palaces, Savitri liked the king and his son. As time went by, she fell in love with Satyavan.

Savitri came back at last to her father's palace. Her parents were pleased that she had found someone that she wanted to marry, even if Satyavan had nothing. As was usual in India, however, they went to see the astrologer. He would study the stars under which Savitri and Satyavan were born and tell what was going to happen to them in the future. The astrologer studied his books for a long time. Then he told the King that the marriage would be a good one. The couple would love each other and care for each other, but, the astrologer said that he had found the name of Satyavan written in the Book of Destiny which Yama had. Yama is the God of Death. It was written in Yama's Book that Satyavan would die within one year.

The King knew that whatever was written in Yama's Book of Destiny could not be altered. The King went to Savitri and begged her to choose someone else. Savitri replied, 'I have given my heart to Satyavan. I can never love another. I will marry him come what may.'

Sadly the King agreed, on condition that Savitri would stay with Satyavan wherever he went. The wedding took place, and the couple went to live with Satyavan's father at the hermitage in the forest. They had much to be sad about. The old king had gone blind. He would never again be king in his own country. Satyavan had less than a year to live. Even so, there was nothing but happiness in the forest. Savitri's smile soon chased away the gloom.

A year passed and it came to the day when the God of Death would come to collect Satyavan. On this day Savitri and Satyavan went together into the forest. As they went further Satyavan's heart was heavy. Suddenly Satyavan clutched his head. He had a dreadful pain. As he fell to the ground Savitri heard the hooves of a buffalo on the forest track and before her appeared a fine strong beast with great horns. On its back, tall and terrible, sat Yama, the God of Death. Yama wore robes of blood-red and carried a king's heavy mace in two of his hands, in a third he held a long sharp trident and in the fourth he had a rope with a noose with which he would drag away the soul of the dead Satyavan. His copper-red eyes stared out from the dark green skin of his face and showed no sign of a smile.

Saying nothing, Yama climbed down from the buffalo and began to tie the noose round Satyavan. When he had done this he remounted the animal and set off, pulling the body of Savitri's husband behind him. Savitri watched as Yama went towards the south, to the Land of the Dead.

Almost running to keep up with the buffalo, Savitri followed. Mile after mile, through forest and over open country, where there was a road and where there was none, Savitri kept up with Yama, following her husband. At last Yama stopped and spoke with some gentleness in his voice, 'Savitri, you must follow me no further. If it is written that a man must die, then die he must. Nothing can change that.'

But Savitri cried out, 'It is written in the Holy Book that not even death can keep a husband and wife apart. I shall stay with you.'

'You must go home,' boomed Yama. 'I will grant you a wish for being so faithful to Satyavan; though you may not wish for his life.'

Savitri asked that Satyavan's blind father should be given back his sight. Yama granted this and set off once more with Satyavan. But Savitri still followed them.

After some time Yama stopped and spoke to Savitri, 'Savitri, I am really sorry for you. I admire the way you love your husband even in death, but I cannot help you. Go back!'

As long as she did not ask for her husband's life, Savitri was given a second wish. She asked that Satyavan's father should be given his kingdom back. The wish was granted.

On went Yama still towards the south. Savitri followed. For a third time, the God of Death stopped the buffalo, climbed down and spoke kindly to Savitri, 'We are not far from the Land of the Dead. There we shall come upon gates that none but the dead may pass. Turn back now for you cannot come into the Land of the Dead.'

For her faithfulness Savitri was granted a third wish as long as she did not ask for Satyavan to be brought back to life. Savitri asked that she should bear a son to be king after the old man died.

'Yes,' said Lord Yama, 'I grant the wish. Now go!'

'But, my Lord,' answered Savitri, 'how can I have a son if I have no husband?'

Yama thought about it. There was no way that he could grant the wish without bringing Satyavan back from the dead. He laughed and admitted that Savitri's faithfulness had conquered death.

Savitri returned to the Land of the Living. When Satyavan awoke he was lying in the forest where he had fallen. Savitri was at his side. 'Come on, Savitri. It's nearly dark you shouldn't have let me sleep so long!' he said joyfully.

As the two came back to the hermitage, they found that the old king had suddenly been given back his sight. Not only that, there was a messenger from the King's own country telling him that the man who had stolen his throne had been killed. The king could now have his throne back.

*

This prayer is heard during Hindu temple services:

Lead us from the darkness to the light.
Lead us from lies to the truth.
Lead us from death to everlasting life.

(from a traditional Hindu devotional prayer)

The Birthday of Krishna
(Janam Astami or Krishnanashtami)

8th of the lunar waning part of the month of Shravan
July/August

Krishna is one of the best-loved Hindu gods, being one of the incarnations of Vishnu, second of the Supreme Trinity. At various times Vishnu has been down to earth to rectify the balance between good and evil in his role as 'the Preserver'. Most Hindus believe that Krishna is the eighth descent of Vishnu and that there are ten altogether (though some say there are over twenty and others that they are innumerable). The seventh incarnation is Rama; the ninth the Buddha, and there is one more still to come before destruction of the world occurs and the cycle of creation begins again.

Krishna was born in Uttar Pradesh at Mathura between Agra and Delhi. Devotees fast the day before and sing at the temple until midnight when his birth is celebrated, especially in central and northern India. After offerings have been made to an image of the god or to a baby Krishna in a flower-bedecked cradle, sweet things are eaten and singing and rejoicing may continue until morning. Krishna is usually depicted as a youth playing a flute and dancing with the girls of his village. He is Lord of the World and lover of all who contemplate him, even in hate. (See also The Festival of Colour-Holi.)

The Birth of Krishna   (7 min.)

The great god, Vishnu, has been to earth a number of times to help when evil seemed to be winning against good. Many Hindus worship Vishnu in the form of Krishna who was Vishnu's eighth appearance in the world.

There was a time when the north of India was ruled by the evil king, Kansa. He was so wicked and cruel and selfish that many people believed he was a demon in the form of a man. The gods watched the cruelties performed by Kansa for as long as they could, until one day the goddess of the Earth begged the Supreme Three Gods to help mankind. The first of the gods, Brahma promised that he would help and sent Vishnu to earth to be born as an ordinary human baby. The child was called Krishna and he grew up to kill the wicked Kansa.

Kansa had a sister, Devaki. She was married to a man called Vasudeva. After the wedding Kansa himself drove Devaki and Vasudeva back to their home. As he whipped up the horses and they galloped along, Kansa heard a voice echo across the skies, saying, 'O Kansa, listen well! The eighth son of

Devaki and Vasudeva will be the cause of your death. Hear this and believe it, O Kansa.'

Immediately Kansa pulled up the horses, drew his sword and seized his sister by her long hair. He was ready to kill her right there. Vasudeva held on to the King's arm and begged him not to. He reminded Kansa that Devaki was his own sister and he flattered him saying that a great king need to take no notice of what he had heard. He pleaded that Devaki's life should be spared. Kansa took no notice and raised his sword to strike. Vasudeva then made a terrible promise.

He promised that if Kansa spared Devaki's life, they would give Kansa any boy children the very minute they were born. Kansa agreed.

As the years went by Devaki gave birth to a number of sons. Kansa had them killed even before they could take their first breath. The years passed and Devaki and Vasudeva began to wonder if they had done the right thing. When Devaki became pregnant for the eighth time, Vasudeva felt no happiness. He knew exactly what would happen if the child was a boy. But the gods had other ideas.

As the time came near for Devaki to give birth, Kansa locked her in prison chained to Vasudeva. Soldiers, elephants, dogs, and lions were put to guard them. There could be no escape. At sunset, Devaki knew that the birth of her baby was near. As the night grew late, storm clouds began to roll across the sky and rain began to fall. The guards had orders to rush in and kill the baby as soon as they heard it cry. But at midnight, when the child was born, the sky echoed with thunder. Lightning flashed and it poured with rain. The guards heard nothing – neither the baby crying nor the sharp snap as Devaki and Vasudeva's chains fell off.

The baby Krishna lay in his cradle, his skin dark like thunderclouds but his eyes bright like the sky. Devaki and Vasudeva knew that theirs was no ordinary child. They bowed their heads and prayed before him. As they did so, the room filled with light and the god Vishnu appeared before them.

'I have appeared like this to show you that your child is I, the Lord Vishnu. It is I who care for the world. It is I who shine like a torch to show men the way to live. I shall save you from your enemies.'

As the vision faded and the room became as dark as the night again, Devaki and Vasudeva were left with their tiny baby in the cradle. But Vasudeva had a plan. He wrapped up the baby and pushed open the door. Outside the animals had run off and the guards were all in a deep sleep. Vasudeva walked straight out. He carried his baby son across the River Yamuna and out into the country to where Nanda, a poor keeper of cows, lived with his wife.

Now Vasudeva had been told by Lord Vishnu that Nanda's wife, Yashoda, would have her baby at the same time as Devaki. He arrived at their poor cottage and found Nanda and Yashoda sleeping. By Yashoda's side there lay a new-born baby girl. Quietly, Vasudeva placed Krishna by Yashoda's side, and the baby girl was wrapped up and taken back to the prison where Devaki was. The guards slept soundly until morning. Whey they found that Devaki had given birth to a girl they left her alone. Kansa's dream had foretold his death by a son of hers, not a daughter.

As King Kansa came to inspect the child, he heard that same haunting voice warning him, 'Hear this, O Kansa! It was said that the eighth son of Devaki and Vasudeva would bring you to your death. You have been tricked, mighty King. Your enemy is alive and well in the city of Mathura.'

That morning in the cow-herd's cottage, Yashoda woke. She remembered that she had given birth to a child the night before, but whether it was a boy or a girl, she couldn't remember. And so Nanda and Yashoda never knew that Krishna was not really their child at all. But then neither was he really Devaki and Vasudeva's: Krishna was the god Vishnu on earth.

So the King of Kings was born to a princess, but he lived his early life amongst the ordinary people of the countryside as the son of a keeper of cows.

*

It was to be many years before Kansa met Krishna, but the end of the story would be as the strange voice had said it would be.

Here is part of the holiest book of the worshippers of Krishna. This is from a speech by Lord Krishna on what God is like and how people should come to him:

I am the ancient wise man, without beginning;
I am the ruler of the worlds and support all life;
I cannot be understood by men –
I am more difficult to understand than the smallest atoms.
I am the cause of the whole world;
It is made by me and destroyed by me.
I live in wisdom in everyone's heart;
I am the goodness of the good.
I am the beginning, and the middle,
I am the end and I am all time,
I am the birth and death of all;
I have made all things out of myself.

Think of me,
Have faith in me,
Adore and worship me,
Meditate upon me,
And you shall come to me.

(from the Bhagavad Gita, c.1st century CE)

Ganesh's Birthday (Ganesh Chaturti)

4th of the month of Bhadrapad
August/September

Ganesh, the popular elephant-headed Hindu god, is worshipped all over India. Particular devotion is given to him in Gujerat and Maharastra in western India where he is regarded by many as the Absolute Reality. As the god of good fortune he is invoked at the beginning of all undertakings, even before the worship of other gods. Ganesh is the god of wisdom and of literature. It was he who wrote down the 'Mahabharata' (about 500 CE), the epic poem telling of the wars of the Bharata clan about 900 BCE, and including the 'Bhagavad Gita', the Song of the Lord which contains the teaching of Lord Krishna.

On the birthday of this benign and well-loved god each family buys a clay image of Ganesh which is carried home on the head. After the image has been worshipped for a week, it is taken to a pool or river and left half-submerged in the water. The family then offers up prayers of farewell. Worship of Ganesh is marked by the offering of coconuts. Their white kernel symbolises purity of mind. Those who pray do so in a kneeling position, arms crossed, and holding the ears. A feature of the belief of his devotees is that of self-sacrifice.

Ganesh Saves the Gods   (3 min.)

There lived a king of the demons called Gajamukha. By praying and fasting he won the favour of the Lord Shiva who granted him a wish. The wish was that he should not be killed by any weapon, by any human, or by any of the lesser gods. Having had his wish granted, Gajamukha was ready to carry out his evil plan which was to rule the world and the lesser gods. He was a wicked and cruel king who made the people of the world bow down in worship to him. Knowing that they could not kill him, even the gods were forced to do whatever Gajamukha commanded. When Gajamukha made them all kneel down before him, crossing their arms and placing their hands over their ears, even Indra, the king of the lesser gods, had to obey.

At last the gods were unable to bear the shame of this any longer. They went with Indra to Mount Kailas, the home of Lord Shiva. They begged him to set them free from the evil of the demon Gajamukha.

In the garden of Shiva's palace stood a temple. On the wall of the temple was carved the holy letter 'Aum' which looks like the twined trunks of two elephants. Shiva told his wife Umadevi, the Mother-Goddess, to stand before the holy sign and concentrate with all her senses.

As the Mother-Goddess stood deep in thought, she took the shape of the holy letter 'Aum'. The letter then became two elephants, a male and a female. From them sprang the holy child, Ganesh. He had five hands, three eyes and the head of an elephant. Umadevi became the goddess again and she and Shiva hugged their strange new son.

Lord Shiva gave Ganesh this command: 'Go and destroy the demon Gujamukha and save the lesser gods from their curse. Then return and stand guard at the gates of our temple.'

Ganesh declared war on the evil demon and many wars were fought against him. Many kinds of weapon were used against Gajamukha but none was successful because of the wish granted to him by Lord Shiva. Finally, in a last terrible battle, Ganesh broke off one of his own tusks, wherein his strength lay, and hurled it at Gajamukha. The demon was pierced through the heart and killed.

The lesser gods realised what a sacrifice Ganesh had made for them and bowed down and worshipped him, kneeling with arms crossed and holding their ears as they had been made to worship Gajamukha.

*

Hindus worship many gods in many different ways believing all the time that they are doing so to find their way to the one true God.

He is One
Who looks after the needs of all peoples at all times,
Who is the beginning and the end of all things;
May he bring us together in friendship.

(from the Svetasvarata Upanishad, c.800 BCE)

The Festival of Durga or The Nine Nights (Durga Puja or Navaratra)

First Month of Asvin
October/November

The Triad of Great Gods: Brahma, the creator of the universe; Vishnu, the preserver of order; and Shiva, the destroyer, who cleans the slate to start again, met in meditation and created a female from their combined thought-energy of white, red, and black brilliance. All three desired her, whereupon she split into three and became Sarasvati, the white goddess, representing the past; Lakshmi, the red goddess, representing the present; and Devi, the black goddess, representing the future.

Sarasvati became Brahma's consort, Lakshmi became the consort of Vishnu, and Devi became Shiva's wife. Thus, just as the Supreme Triad are all aspects of one God, so their consorts are one and the same, created by God of God himself.

Durga is one of the many forms of Shiva's wife, Devi (or Mahadevi, the Great Goddess). She is seen in different roles, having different names and appearances. As Parvati, she is the beautiful and faithful wife of Shiva; as Uma, she is the goddess of light and beauty; as Kali (the Black), she is hideous and terrible; as Devi, she is the goddess of fertility.

Durga Puja is also known as Navaratra, the Nine Nights, because this is how long it lasts. It begins on the night of the first of Asvin. Celebrated mainly in Bengal, Durga Puja is the occasion when daughters return to their parents' homes and are welcomed with feasting and the giving of presents.

Durga, the divine mother and personification of fertility, is worshipped in the nine manifestations she undertook in order to defeat a demon. She is worshipped in various ways during the first seven days of the festival. On the eighth day, joyful celebrations begin, which reach their climax on the ninth day, Dusshera. Dusshera, the Ten Days (q.v.), marks the end of Durga Puja and the beginning of the festivities which culminate in Divali, the Festival of Lights (q.v.).

Durga Defeats the Forces of Evil   (3 min.)

Durga is the wife of the great god Shiva in one of her many forms. She was born fully grown as a very beautiful woman. She has ten arms. Durga was created by the three Great Gods to defend the heavens against the threat of a terrible devil. This devil was tremendously powerful and had conquered the earth, the sky, and the heavens. The lesser gods, led by their king, Indra, had been chased down to earth and spent their time hiding in forests. The devil stopped the people on earth from worshipping the gods and even from reading the holy books or saying their prayers.

Terrible things happened. Rain fell when it shouldn't. It was dry in the wet season. Rivers flooded and went the wrong way. Fire burned cold and the stars in the night sky went out. The earth cried out for order to be put back again.

In her ten hands Durga carried weapons of the gods. She had the thunderbolt of flame and lightning that belonged to Indra. She had a burning arrow from Agni, the god of fire. She had a garland of snakes from the snake-god, Shesha, and the sharp trident, a three-pronged long fork, of Shiva. She rode not on a horse, but on a large and fierce lion from the Himalayan mountains.

As soon as she appeared, an army of thousands of the devil's slaves and demons met her with a hail of arrows. They flung rocks at her and even tore up trees and flung them too. Durga blasted most of the devil's army with a flaming brand of fire and many were killed. The Devil himself charged straight for the goddess who managed to knock aside his club and spear as he charged. She struck him to the ground and held him under her foot.

Struggling violently, the devil escaped from Durga and returned to his camp. Meanwhile the goddess destroyed the rest of the devil's army. Running, jumping and hiding, and changing shape all the time, the devil attacked again. He hurled a mountain at Durga which she split into many pieces. Finally, the devil changed into the form of a huge buffalo which rolled down rocks on to Durga, but she speared him with Shiva's trident. As she pinned him to the ground, he turned back into his normal shape, that of a devil with a thousand arms. Still holding him, Durga fitted an arrow to her bow with two of her other hands and fired it through his evil heart. And so good triumphed over evil.

*

Hindus believe that there are many gods and goddesses but that they all represent one God. This hymn shows that:

O Lord of all, praise to you!
You are the soul of everything,
You are everything that happens,
You are all life, Lord of pleasure and happiness.

O Lord of peace, praise to you!
Praise to you, O hidden Lord,
Unimaginable, unthinkable,
Lord without begining and with no end.

(from Kutsayana's 'Hymn of Praise' from the Maitri Upanishad)

The Ten Days (Dusshera)

9th of the month of Asvin
October/November

Dusshera is the period of ten days which culminate in the festival of Divali, the Festival of Lights (q.v.) and is celebrated by dramatised episodes from the life of

Rama, performed by travelling players. Lord Rama is the seventh descent to earth of the god Vishnu whose purpose was to defeat the demon-king of Lanka (known until recently as Ceylon, now Sri Lanka). Rama was the son and heir of the King of Ayodhya (now in the state of Uttar Pradesh), but was banished because of his step-mother's jealous connivance (see Rama's Birthday). After many hardships, Rama, helped by his faithful wife, Sita, defeated the demon, Ravana. During the festival huge paper effigies of Ravana are burned to celebrate the victory of good over evil. (see Divali, the Festival of Lights for the story of Rama's return, the sequel to this story.)

Rama Defeats the Demon Ravana   (8 min.)

Rama and his wife Sita had been forced to leave the land where Rama should have been king. Rama had asked Sita not to follow him to face unknown dangers, but she went all the same, saying that a wife's place is by her husband's side. For some time they lived in the great forest.

While Rama and Sita passed their time in the forest an army was marching about the land causing misery and terror wherever it went. At its head was the wicked demon-king Ravana. Ravana had heard of Sita's beauty and was determined to make her his wife.

Being a demon, Ravana had the power to use certain magic spells. He sent into the forest, close to where Rama and Sita were resting, a most beautiful deer. As soon as she saw the deer Sita wanted Rama to capture it for her. He gave chase. But each time he came near the deer seemed to be a long way ahead again. Deeper and deeper into the forest went Rama never getting any closer to the deer. As soon as Rama was out of sight Ravana swooped down in his flying chariot, his ten heads grinning wickedly. He seized Sita and made off with her through the skies back to the island of Lanka where he was king. At last Rama came back from deep in the forest to where he had left his wife. Sita was gone.

As Sita was being taken through the sky to Lanka in Ravana's chariot, Jatayu, King of the Vultures heard her cries for help. He flew up to attack the demon, but, though he fought hard, Jatayu was fatally wounded and the chariot sped on its way. As he searched for Sita, Rama came across the dying bird. Jatayu hardly had breath to speak, but he managed to explain to Rama what had happened – and then he died.

Rama said, 'He died for my sake, and he who dies for my sake must go to the highest heaven.'

Although Rama was anxious to chase after the demon, Ravana, he built a proper funeral fire for the King of the Birds and prayed for his soul.

On the way Rama made friends with a monkey called Sugriva. Sugriva had once been king in the land of monkeys, but, like Rama, the throne had been taken from him. Sugriva promised Rama the help of all the monkey people if Rama would first free them from the wicked Bali. After a struggle and some fighting Bali was defeated and killed. Sugriva now kept his promise and gathered a vast army of monkeys together. Led by Rama and Sugriva they travelled until they reached the sea. Beyond it lay the kingdom of Lanka.

Sugriva ordered his monkey general, Hanuman, to fly across the water to spy on Ravana's fortress and to find where Sita was. He found Sita in the gardens. Ravana had threatened to kill her and eat her if she would not be his wife, but Sita had refused. Hanuman told Sita of the plans to rescue her. Delighted with how well things were going, Hanuman jumped and leaped excitedly all around Ravana's garden pulling up the plants and scattering the flowers. When it was reported by his guards that a monkey was destroying his beautiful garden, Ravana sent his soldiers to stop him. After a short but fierce fight Hanuman was seized and dragged before the ten-headed demon-king.

However, playful though he was, Hanuman was a monkey of great intelligence with a very quick mind. He told Ravana that he had been sent as a messenger from Rama and that any real king would not dream of harming a messenger sent by the enemy. This was quite right of course and so Ravana listened to what Hanuman had to say.

But Ravana grew angrier with every word the monkey general spoke. Fearlessly Hanuman scorned the wicked and cruel things that Ravana had done. Ravana lost his temper with the brave and cheeky monkey, shouting, 'There may be a law to say that I cannot kill an enemy messenger, but there is nothing to stop me from punishing his rudeness. A monkey's tail is very precious to him. Guards! Tie oily rags round his tail and set fire to them.'

As the rags were lit Hanuman leaped out of the grasp of the guards and jumped out of the window. He ran round the rooftops of the city, his tail burning behind him. Every building he landed on began to catch fire, and before Hanuman left the island, the whole place was burning fiercely. The demons rushed around madly not knowing which fire to put out first.

As Hanuman came back to the mainland where Rama was with Sugriva's monkey army, they had just finished building a bridge across the sea. The last few stones and boulders were hurled into place and then men and monkeys swarmed over to attack the demon army.

The battle was long and hard. Many demons were killed by the monkey army. Many monkeys were eaten by a giant demon. Twice Rama himself was captured but the clever Hanuman helped him to escape. At last all the demon generals were killed and the fight was betweem Rama and Ravana alone.

Ravana was horrible to look at. He was huge in size and he had ten wicked-looking heads. As Rama cut off one head another immediately grew in its place. There seemed to be no way of killing the demon. During a rest in the fight Rama quickly took a special arrow from his quiver. He had been waiting for the chance to use it for it had been blessed and given to him by the gods. The fire of the sun burned in its point, the speed of the wind was in its flight, and the weight of the mountain of heaven was behind the force of Rama's shot. As it struck Ravana in the heart, he staggered backwards. From each of his ten ugly heads came a deathly scream. And then the Demon King fell to the ground, dead.

Rama wiped the sweat from his forehead and breathed a deep sigh of relief. The sound of the gods singing their hymns of praise to him could be heard from afar. Rama had defeated evil and Sita could be with him once again.

*

This hymn is to the God Vishnu. Rama was Vishnu in human form on earth.

Wherever I go you are my friend;
You take my hand and guide me.

As I walk along I lean on you
And you travel with me and carry my load.

When I say foolish things in temper
You control me and take away my shame.

Now I know that every man is a friend of mine,
I pray like a happy child,
For I feel your joy within me and around me.

(by Tukaram 1608–1649)

Festival of Lights (Divali or Deepawali)

The last two days of the month of Asvin and
the fist two days of the month of Kartik
October/November

Divali is probably the greatest Hindu festival. It is celebrated all over India. For some it is the New Year, depending on the calendar used. It is also the time of the summer harvest. The word 'deepawali' means literally 'a cluster of lights'. On this occasion all houses are lit inside and out so that the goddess of good fortune, Lakshmi, consort of Vishnu, will visit them. Fireworks and firecrackers are set off, to keep away the evil spirits. Presents, especially sweetmeats, are exchanged and relatives visit one another.

For most Hindus, the festival is associated with the return of Rama and Sita after their fourteen years of exile (see Rama's Birthday) and is the culmination of Dusshera, the Ten Days (q.v.). In the Mahratha States, people remember the defeat by Vishnu of the demon Bali, while Bengalis pay homage to the souls of the dead.

Rama and Sita Return   (3 min.)

Rama had defeated the evil of Ravana, the demon-king of Lanka. Sita, his wife, had been captured by Ravana who tried to make her marry him. He had even threatened her with death, but still she refused. But when Sita came to Rama, everyone was amazed and rather upset that he would have nothing to do with her.

'How do I know that you did not give in and marry Ravana when I wasn't there?' said Rama. 'How do I know that you have been true and faithful to me?'

Everyone asked Rama how he could say such a terrible thing after Sita had been so brave, but he wouldn't listen.

At last Sita spoke, 'I shall undergo ordeal by fire,' she said. 'Bring wood to burn. Pile it up and set fire to it. If I have not been true to Rama, my husband, the flames will burn me to death. If I have been faithful, the gods will protect me.'

The wood was piled high, but no one wanted to light the fire. At last Rama ordered it to be done. As the flames licked fiercely towards the sky Sita stepped on to the blazing pile. The soldiers cried openly and begged Rama to save her, but as they watched, the flames seemed to lift Sita up. She stood on the flames smiling and as bright as the morning sun. Rama helped her down from the fire, unharmed.

'I believed you had been true to me all the time, Sita,' he said, 'but who else would have have believed us? It had to be proved, and it has been proved. Now we can return to our homeland.'

Rama and Sita thanked the monkeys who had helped them to defeat the evil demons. Then they began their long journey home. The fourteen years that they had been forced to spend away from their kingdom of Ayodhya were over. Rama was returning to be king.

Crowds cheered as Rama returned to the palace. He entered to meet his brother, Bharata, who had ruled in his place. Bharata took Rama to the throne and showed him Rama's shoes which he had placed there to remind him that he was only acting as king until the real king, Rama, returned.

Rama was crowned at a great coronation with Sita sitting by his side. There was happiness and rejoicing throughout the land.

Vamana the Dwarf-god   (5 min.)

The god Vishnu has been to earth a number of times to help mankind in the fight of good against evil. The seventh time he came was as prince Rama, the eighth time was as Krishna, but the fifth time was as a dwarf named Vamana.

Vamana was born while a certain king ruled, a king by the name of Bali. Bali seemed to be a very religious man – he went to the temple very often, he gave money to the priests and he always could be seen saying his prayers at the right time. He was the most powerful king in India, and he only had one fault. Because there were no countries left for him to conquer on earth, Bali had decided that he was also going to be ruler of heaven. And so Vishnu was born as the dwarf Vamana to save the gods.

While Vamana was growing up, Bali took over the heavenly kingdom. Indra and the lesser gods were driven out. Now only Vamana could save the day.

Vamana was born into a tribe of priests. His father was a priest and so he too became a priest. One day Vamana came to Bali while the King was praying by the side of a river. King Bali smiled to himself as he saw the little man coming towards him but when he saw the mark of a priest on Vamana's forehead, he bowed low before him and asked if he could offer him help in any way. Priests are treated with great respect in India.

Vamana sat down on the river bank beside the King.

'Yes, there is a gift you can make me. You are famous for being kind and generous to those who are in need, and I shall not ask for any more than I need.'

'Ask for what you want then, priest,' answered Bali.

'I shall ask you for a piece of land, but I only want as much land as I can cover in three steps.'

'Three steps,' laughed Bali, looking down at the dwarf's short legs. 'Is that all?'

'A wise man does not take more than he needs,' replied Vamana.

Now if Bali had had time to think before he said 'yes', he might have realised that the last comment was about him. Bali had far more than he needed. He was the most powerful king in the world and he now ruled heaven. But Bali did not have time to think. As Vamana took his first step he grew and grew until his head disappeared into the clouds. With this step he covered the whole of the earth. He carried on growing and with his second step he covered the kingdom of heaven. From the skies above, King Bali heard a thunderous voice calling down: 'Well, King, I have only taken two steps and I have crossed the whole universe. And yet you promised me three. Where shall I take my third step?'

As Bali looked up and saw the gigantic foot of Vamana the dwarf, he knew that it was really Vishnu who was speaking to him and he knew that Vishnu's third step would be on top of him. Bali was hurled into the depths of hell, and there he is to this day.

*

When Lord Vishnu visits the earth, whether as Vamana, Rama or Krishna, he is always seen as a man of action. He spends his time doing things. This poem by a great modern Indian poet, Rabindranath Tagore, says the same thing:

   Leave this chanting and singing and telling of beads! Whom dost thou worship in this lonely dark corner of a temple with all doors shut? Open thine eyes and see thy God is not before thee! He is there where the tiller is tilling the hard ground and where the path-maker is breaking stones. (Gitanjali, poem II)

Jewish Festivals

The Fast of Esther

13th of the month of Adar
February/March

The story relating to this fast, and also to the Feast of Purim on the following day, can be found in the Book of Esther. Esther was a Jewess married to King Ahasuerus (Xerxes I c.519–465 CE) of Persia (modern Iran). Ahasuerus's minister, Haman, planned to destroy all the Jews in Persia. Esther prevented this.

In Persia at this time there were many Jews. After the Babylonian King, Nebuchadrezzar, had conquered Jerusalem, he deported perhaps 50,000 to Babylon (586 BCE). When Cyrus II of Persia captured Babylon (538 BCE) he encouraged enslaved peoples to return to their countries of origin. He even gave back captured religious objects. However, many Jews had settled in Persia and had no reason to return to Israel. Jews who did not return to their native land moved to many parts of the world and are called Jews of the Diaspora or Dispersion.

I have divided the story between the festival of the Fast of Esther and that of Lots, Purim (q.v.). This part is not complete without the other.

Esther the Jewess Becomes Queen of Persia   (9 min.)

Esther was the daughter of a Jew who lived in Persia about two thousand five hundred years ago. Her Hebrew name was Hadassah, which means myrtle; Esther was her Persian name. While she was still young both her father and mother died so Esther was taken care of by her older cousin, Mordecai. They lived at Shushan not far from the king's palace. As Esther grew up, she became not only beautiful, but kind and thoughtful as well.

Now it happened that King Ahasuerus had a terrible argument with his wife, the queen. He divorced her and commanded his soldiers to bring before him the most beautiful girls in the land so that he might choose a new wife for himself.

As the soldiers looked around the streets of Shushan, they came across Esther. They informed her of the King's command and told her to go to the palace. Esther was filled with alarm.

'You must certainly go to the palace,' said Mordecai, 'but do not tell the King that you are a Jewess.'

Esther made herself ready and set out at once. All over the country, hundreds of other girls were doing the same thing. From tiny villages, from towns, and from large cities they came to Shushan. Each one hoped that King Ahasuerus might find her the most beautiful, and choose her for his queen.

At the palace, the girls were bathed in sweet-smelling bath oils and dressed in fine clothes.

King Ahasuerus sat in the throne room and called for the girls one by one. Each was asked if she would like a gift, and whatever she asked for was given to her. When Esther's turn came the King's servants asked what she would like.

'Nothing', replied Esther. 'I have been looked after very well, thank you. I do not need anything else.'

King Ahasuerus was impressed by Esther's beauty and quiet dignity. After he had seen all the girls, he sent for her again and asked her to marry him. Esther agreed.

After they had been married for some months, the King came to love Esther so much that he decided to crown her as his queen. Esther, the Jewish orphan girl who had been looked after by her cousin, now became Queen of the land of Persia.

Although Esther was queen, however, it did not change her; she was still kind and thoughtful. Every day she went to the palace gate to see her cousin Mordecai. Again and again Mordecai urged her never to mention to the King that she was Jewish nor tell him who her family was.

One day while Mordecai was quietly waiting for Esther to come to the palace gate, he overheard two of the King's officials plotting to kill Ahasuerus. The two men hurried away as Queen Esther appeared. Of course, Mordecai told his cousin about the plot, and Esther promised to warn the King at once.

She went to her husband: 'Your Majesty,' she said. 'I have been told by a man called Mordecai that two of your ministers are plotting to kill you. Mordecai is a man trusted in the city and so I believe him.'

'I shall put my police on to it straight away,' said the King.

After making secret investigations, Ahasuerus's police found that it was true. The two officials were arrested and executed.

Not long after this, a man called Haman began to gain favour with the King. Haman worked hard and the King began to rely on him, giving him more and more important jobs to do. At last, Ahasuerus made Haman his Chief Minister. Then he sent out a notice to the people telling them that they must bow low before their new Chief Minister as he passed by.

As Haman came out of the gates of the palace there stood Mordecai waiting to see his cousin, Queen Esther. Servants, soldiers, and passers-by bowed as the Chief Minister came proudly by – everyone bowed low, except for one man:

'I bow only to the Lord my God,' said Mordecai.

Haman was furious that Mordecai was not impressed by his importance. He found out all he could about Mordecai. When he learned that Mordecai was a Jew Haman was filled with hatred for all Jews. He began to think that the Jews were far too proud and that they should be destroyed.

Gradually, Haman told Ahasuerus stories about a certain group of people in the kingdom who were not keeping the laws. He told the King that these people were Jews; that they were making their own laws and plotting against him. This was not true. The Jews were a law-abiding people and as foreigners in Persia they were rather careful to behave themselves. But Haman's plan was working, and the King was beginning to worry.

The Persians believed that some days were luckier than others and that there were right days and wrong days to do things. When anything special had to be done it was important to do it on a good day, or a lucky day. To find out which these days were, a system of lots was used.

Day by day, Haman had been casting lots. Finally, in the last month of the year, he drew out a lot which told him that the time was right for his evil plot to be hatched. He went to the King and once more reminded him about the people who were causing trouble in the land. The King asked Haman what he should do, for Ahasuerus trusted Haman's advice.

'Sign this letter giving me permission to do what I think best,' said Haman. 'I will deal with these people.'

The worried King signed the letter. Immediately Haman went away and sent messages to all the governors of all the provinces of the land written in every language spoken by the people. In every market-place in Persia the Jews read the notices and they could not believe what they saw. The notice said that on the thirteenth day of the month, every Jew, young or old, man or child, would be killed, and that the King would take all their money and land.

Haman said that no Jew would escape. He had no idea that the King's own wife was Jewish. (Continued as the story of Lots, Purim.)

The Eighteen Blessings of the Jewish Prayer Book are very well known, and the first and last three are used in synagogue services, at festivals, and on many other occasions. This prayer is from the Seventh Blessing:

Look on us in our troubles,
Support us and be quick to save us,
O God, our King and mighty Saviour.
Blessed is our God, the Saviour of Israel.

(from the Amidah, *c*.500 BCE)

*

With much love you have loved us, O Lord our God;
With great pity you have pitied us.
O Father, our King,
for the sake of our fathers
who trusted in you
and who learnt the laws of life from you,
be gracious to us and teach us also.
O Father, our merciful Father, always sympathetic,
have mercy upon us.

(from the Amidah, *c*.500 BCE)

Lots (Purim)

14th of the month of Adar
February/March

While the day before Purim is a fast commemorating Queen Esther's fast, the Feast of the Lots is a day of rejoicing. The lots referred to were cast by Haman, Chief Minister of King Ahasuerus of Persia, to decide which day was most propitious for the extermination of the Jews. In Jewish homes festival meals are eaten and gifts are given to the poor. A feature of the festival meal is a three-cornered cake which contains poppy seeds. In the synagogues the Scroll of Esther is read and a loud noise made by the congregation at the mention of Haman's name. In Israel carnivals are held and Jews around the world act out plays showing the defeat of the wicked Haman and the triumph of Esther.

Esther Saves the Persian Jews   (6 min.)

The Chief Minister of Ahasuerus, Haman, had lied and tricked the King into believing that the Jews were not obeying the laws of the land. Haman had sent out a notice to all of Persia that the Jews were all to be killed on the 13th of the month.

In the streets of the capital city, Shushan, Jews were weeping and crying out to be saved. There was such a noise and commotion that Queen Esther wanted to know what the noise was about.

Esther sent a servant down to see her cousin, Mordecai, who was waiting at the palace gates. Mordecai sent the message back that the Jews were all to be killed. He reminded Esther that she was a Jewess and that Haman's plot would also include her.

But Queen Esther did not need reminding. She sent the message to Mordecai that all the Jews of the city of Shushan should fast, eating no food for three days. She too would fast and then go to the King to see what could be done.

After the three days Esther went to her husband and invited him and his Minister, Haman, to come to a feast the following day. The King gladly accepted, for he loved his wife. Haman, too, accepted. As Haman left the palace he passed Mordecai at the gate. As usual Mordecai refused to bow to Haman and, as usual, Haman burned with anger but did nothing. When Haman got home he ordered a very tall gallows to be built on which Mordecai would hang in the morning. Haman thought that this would make him feel much happier when he went to the Queen's feast the next day.

That night the King could not sleep. He ordered his servant to bring the records of the royal court for him to read to make him sleepy and, as he read, he came across the name of Mordecai the Jew. He remembered that Mordecai had saved his life by telling Queen Esther that two of his officals were planning to kill him. Ahasuerus searched the records but he could find nowhere that Mordecai had been rewarded.

When Haman came to court the next day, King Ahasuerus asked him, 'How should I treat a man that has pleased the King?'

Haman thought that the King was talking about Haman himself, and said: 'You should give him your royal clothes, set on his head the royal crown, and send him through the streets of the city for all the people to cheer.'

'Well,' said the King, 'that is how I shall treat the Jew, Mordecai, who saved my life. See to it at once, Haman.'

Haman was dumbfounded. Inwardly he seethed with anger but he had to do as he was told. And so Mordecai was taken through the streets dressed very finely. When Haman looked at the gallows where Mordecai should have been hanging he went home in misery. But he did not have time to be miserable for long, for the King's messengers came to take him to the feast that Queen Esther had prepared. Haman did not want to go – but he had no choice.

Worse was to come. King Ahasuerus was pleased with the feast and pleased with his wife. He offered to give the Queen a favour. 'Just ask, Queen Esther, and I shall give you any favour – even if it is half my kingdom.'

'O King, I ask you to give me my life and the life of my people, for we are about to die.'

Queen Esther went on to explain to the King that she was a Jewess and that Haman had lied and tricked the King into believing that the Jews were plotting against him. Haman was the guilty one.

Ahasuerus loved Esther so greatly that he believed her. Nor did he mind that Esther was a Jewess and not a true Persian. He ordered that Haman should be taken away and hanged on the same gallows that had been prepared for Mordecai.

Esther had saved her cousin, herself, and all the Jews of Persia.

*

This prayer is one of the Eighteen Blessings which is recited three times each day. It is a prayer of thanks to God.

We give you thanks, O Lord our God,
And the God of our fathers;

Our lives are built on you
And you protect us so that we might be saved.
We give you thanks and sing your praise,
For our lives are in your hands,
And our souls are in your safe-keeping;

For your miracles and for your wonders,
For your gifts to us, we give you thanks at all times,
Evening, morning and midday.
You are good, for your loving-kindness never fails;
You are merciful, for your mercies never fail;
All people praise your great name,
For you are good, O God.
Blessed is our Lord
And it is beautiful to sing his praises always.

(from the Amidah prayer, c.500 BCE)

The Passover (Pesach)

15th–21st of the month of Nisan
March/April

In Biblical times the Passover was kept for seven days. Later, outside Israel, an extra day was added which is still kept by the Orthodox, though not by Progessive Jews. This very important festival commemorates the time when the Israelites were the slaves of the Egyptians. Moses led his people to safety across the Red Sea after the Angel of Death had killed the first-born of every Egyptian family and spared the Israelites by passing over their houses. Moses was born in Egypt and brought up by a royal Egyptian princess, but his nursemaid was his own mother and so he was always aware of his origins within the Jewish slave community. Thothmes III (ruled 1501–1448 BCE) was Pharaoh when Moses escaped from Egypt after killing a slave driver. Amenhotep II (1448–1420 BCE) was the pharaoh who suffered the plagues.

At Passover, Jews eat special meals which include unleavened bread (the Egyptians demanded their immediate departure so their bread had no time to rise). At family reunions the youngest asks questions about the origin and meaning of the feast and is answered in a traditional form by the head of the household. Formerly in Israel the festival was one of the three occasions of pilgrimage to the Temple of Jerusalem.

The Jews Leave Egypt   (4 min.)

Moses grew up in Egypt in the household of Pharoah's daughter, but he knew he was an Israelite by birth. One day he killed an Egyptian who was ill-treating an Israelite slave, and fled to Midian. Here he married the daughter of Jethro, a village priest.

One day, as he was looking after his father-in-law's flocks in the desert he came to Horeb, the mountain sacred to God. There he saw a bush burning fiercely. This was not unusual – in the heat sometimes fires were caused. But this bush did not seem to be burning to ashes. It kept on burning and did not go out. While he stared in wonder at the burning bush, Moses heard God calling him out of the fire.

God told him that he was to go back to set free the Jewish slaves. Moses was afraid and reluctant, but whatever excuses he found, God had an answer for him. Full of fear Moses set out for the land of Egypt from which he had run away.

Moses went to the royal palace and said to Pharaoh, 'The Lord God of Israel says, "Let my people go."'

Pharaoh just laughed: 'Let them go?' he said. 'Certainly not. Who is this God of Israel to tell me what to do? The Jewish slaves are needed to build my pyramids and temples. But I'll tell you what I will do – I will make them work harder!'

The Israelites were furious with Moses. Of course, he had not set them free. How could he? What was worse, they were being made to work harder and the soldiers bullied them even more.

Moses prayed to God for help and returned to Pharaoh to threaten him that if he did not let the Israelites go free the River Nile and all the waters of Egypt would be turned to blood. All the fish would die. The rivers would stink and the Egyptians would be unable to drink any of the water. Angrily Pharaoh refused and Moses immediately turned the river red. For seven days the water remained like this – but Pharaoh was angry and still refused to free the slaves.

Then Moses made the land swarm with frogs; they swarmed into the villages and towns. They swarmed into houses and even in the royal palace of Pharaoh. They got into bedrooms and in beds; in the ovens and even in the bread. In desperation Pharaoh promised to let the Israelites go. But as soon as the frogs had gone, he changed his mind: 'The Israelites will remain my slaves,' he said.

God gave Moses the power to send plagues of lice, flies, and cattle disease. All the Egyptian herds died, but none of the Israelites' cattle became ill.

God sent a plague of boils on the Egyptians, a storm of hailstones which ruined all the Egyptian crops, a plague of locusts which ate what green plants remained. These clouds of locusts were so thick that they turned the sky black, but not so black as the three days of darkness which God sent to the land of Egypt. Each time Pharaoh promised that he would let the slaves go out of Egypt, but when the plague stopped, Pharaoh changed his mind.

God promised Moses that one final plague would make Pharaoh keep his promise. Moses called all the people of Israel together.

'You must mark your doorposts with the blood of a freshly killed lamb or kid-goat. Tonight the Angel of Death will pass over the land of Egypt and kill the first-born son of every house where there is no mark. After this, Pharaoh will set you free.'

The Israelites did what Moses told them and, at midnight, death came to Egypt. From the palace of Pharaoh himself to the poorest home in the land, the eldest son of every family was struck dead.

In the middle of the night, Pharaoh sent for Moses: 'Get out of my land. Take your people, and take your flocks and herds. Leave my land for ever.'

The Israelites hurriedly cooked themselves something to eat. They did not have time to let the bread rise properly and so they took it flat and heavy as it was. They packed the few things they had and set off with Moses away from the land of Egypt. At last they were free.

*

After the Israelites had been saved, the people danced to the Lord to show their thanks, while Moses sang what is now called 'The Song of the Sea'.

> I will sing to the Lord,
> For he has risen up in triumph;
> He has hurled horses and riders into the sea.
> The Lord is my safety and my protection;
> He has shown that he is my saviour.
> He is my God, and I will sing his glory;
> He is my father's God, and I will sing his praise.
> The Lord shall reign for ever and ever.

(from the Book of Exodus of the Torah, *c.*1000 BCE)

The Feast of Weeks (Shavuot or Pentecost)

6–7th of the month of Sivan
May/June

Before the destruction of the Temple in 70 CE Shavuot was an occasion of pilgrimage to Jerusalem. On the second day of the Passover Festival barley had been carried into the Temple and offered to God. Now the first fruits of the harvest were brought in, fifty days later – hence the Feast of Weeks is sometimes referred to as Pentecost (Greek for fifty). Synagogues are decorated with fruits and flowers, some Progressive congregations hold confirmation services and many synagogues hold midnight study sessions.

The Feast is associated with God's giving the Ten Commandments to Moses (c.1400 BCE) on Mount Sinai (Egypt). To Jews this represents a particular revelation of God to their people. Traditional readings are heard in synagogues from the Book of Ruth, the latter being one who accepted utterly the Jewish commandments. Stories are told of King David (ruled c.1012–972 BCE), Ruth's great grandson, who died at the Feast of Weeks.

The Ten Commandments   (6 min.)

It was three months since Moses had led the Jewish slaves to freedom. Times had been hard enough when the Israelites were slaves in Egypt. Now they were free, things hardly seemed much better. Many of the people grumbled about travelling and never seeming to get anywhere; others were beginning to starve, and some started to think they were better off as slaves. And now, three months and many miles later, the Israelites came with Moses to the wilderness of Sinai, a place of rocks and hills where there was no water and very few plants. There, close to Mount Sinai, they made their camp.

Moses climbed to the top of the mountain when God spoke to him. When he came down he gave his people God's message: they should go and pray to God, then come again to the mountain in three days' time dressed in their best clothes. God would show himself in a sign to them.

On the third day the people of Israel came to the bottom of Mount Sinai, having done as Moses had told them. The mountain was covered in thick cloud, and thunder and lightning shattered the quiet of the desert. Fire began to burn on the sides of the mountain and smoke filled the air. Suddenly a loud trumpet sounded and the mountain shook as if there was an earthquake. The people heard the voice of God call down to Moses telling him to come up the mountain.

Moses climbed through the smoke and the cloud. God spoke to him. He gave Moses Ten Commandments for the people of Israel to live by.

As the thunder rolled louder and the smoke on the mountain grew thicker, the people of Israel became afraid and moved away, while Moses climbed higher to pray with God.

While Moses was on Mount Sinai flames burst from it like a volcano and smoke poured into the sky for six days. When the prophet came down he wrote down the laws for the people of Israel.

These are the Ten Commandments:

1   I am the Lord your God who set you free from slavery in Egypt.
2   You shall have no other gods but me and you shall not worship statues.
3   You shall not swear by the name of God falsely.
4   Remember the Sabbath day and keep it holy.
5   Honour your father and your mother.
6   You shall not kill.
7   You shall not be unfaithful to your husband or wife.
8   You shall not steal.
9   You shall not tell lies about anyone.
10   You shall not want other people's things.

Again Moses climbed the mountain and this time he was away for forty days and nights. At first the people thought he must be talking with God. Then they began to get worried, and finally they believed that he must not be coming back.

'Moses has left us,' they said.

Others said, 'God has left us.'

'Let us make a statue to the old gods,' said some. 'We need a god that we can see.'

It was agreed. The people brought whatever gold they had to Aaron, who was one of their leaders and the brother of Moses. The gold was thrown into a great cooking pot and melted. A huge calf, like the statues of gods that the Israelites had seen in Egypt, was built of wood. When it was finished the gold was made into sheets and the calf was covered with it.

Aaron made an altar in front of the golden calf and said, 'Tomorrow shall be the day we worship the golden calf. Be sure to bring something to give our god.'

The next day fires were burned and animals were sacrificed to the golden calf. The people prayed to it and worshipped it.

At the top of Mount Sinai Moses wrote the Ten Commandments on tablets of stone. It was time for him to come down from the mountain. When he reached the bottom, and found the people dancing around the golden calf, he lost his temper. While he had been up the mountain worshipping God, they were down here worshipping a statue. Had they turned away from God and forgotten his laws already? Moses smashed the tablets on the ground. He pushed over and broke up the golden calf, burning it on the fire that stood before it.

Once again Moses climbed the mountain to ask forgiveness for his people. He stayed away for another forty days and nights, and for a second time he returned with the Ten Commandments written on two tablets. He told the Israelites that God was a merciful God and that they were indeed forgiven.

The Israelites built a special altar of wood which they could carry round with them on their journey through the desert. In it they put the stone tablets on which were written the Ten Commandments, so that they would never again forget the word of God.

The Story of Ruth   (4 min.)

Elimelech and his wife, Naomi, left their home town of Bethlehem to travel to the land of Moab because there was famine in their own country. With them went their two sons, Mahlon and Chilion. The hungry times in Bethlehem passed, but Elimelech stayed on in Moab. Here he had settled down with his family. When the boys became old enough they both married girls of Moab. Mahlon married Orpah and Chilion married a girl called Ruth.

After ten years, tragedy struck; Elimelech died suddenly. And then the two sons, who had never been strong, became ill and also died. Naomi was left in a foreign land with no husband and no family to look after her.

Naomi could do nothing else but return to the land from which she came. She called Ruth and Orpah together and asked them to go back to their families. 'You are still young; you can start new lives in your own homes.'

'But we must stay with you. You are our family now.'

'I can't look after you. Go back home,' said Naomi. 'May the Lord be kind to you, as you have been kind to me and to my sons.'

Weeping, Orpah kissed her mother-in-law and turned to go, but Ruth would not leave. 'Don't make me go. Wherever you go, I will go, and wherever you stay, I will stay. Your people shall be my people, and your God shall be my God. Where you die, I will die, and there will I be buried. Nothing but death shall part us.'

And so Ruth went back with Naomi to Bethlehem.

Ruth and her mother-in-law came back to Bethlehem just at the beginning of the harvest. As they passed alongside the fields, the people were beginning to cut the barley and taking it to be stored.

Now, in Bethlehem there was a rich relation of Naomi's husband, a man called Boaz. While the reapers were in Boaz's field cutting the barley harvest, Ruth went to Boaz and asked him if she might glean all the ears of the barley that the reapers had missed.

Boaz said she could. 'You can pick any grains that you find in my fields. And when you are thirsty, come to drink from our water; and when you are hungry, come and eat our bread.'

'Why do you treat me so kindly?' asked Ruth. 'I am a foreigner in this country and a stranger to you.'

'I have heard of you. You married the son of a relation of mine and I have heard how you left your country and your own mother and father and came to this land to look after your old mother-in-law. The God of Israel will look after you now.'

Boaz went to his reapers and told them that they must let Ruth glean as much grain as she could, and that they should let handfuls drop where she might find them.

So Ruth went each day to glean what she could from the fields of Boaz. She stayed with Naomi, her mother-in-law, and they lived quite well from the barley they collected. The time came when all the barley had been gathered in and a great party was to be held to celebrate the end of the harvest.

Naomi told Ruth to get ready to go to the party. She told Ruth not to speak to Boaz unless he spoke to her, and when the party was over and everyone lay down on the floor to sleep, Ruth should lie down not far from Boaz.

Ruth went to the party. When it was over and everyone lay down to sleep,

Ruth did as Naomi had said. At midnight Boaz awoke and found Ruth asleep near him. Boaz asked Ruth to marry him. There was a problem, however. It was the custom for the closest relative of a man who had died to marry the dead man's wife. Boaz was not the closest relative – there was one man closer.

The next day Boaz met the relative and discussed the matter with him.

'Hello, cousin,' said Boaz. 'Of course you know that our relative Elimelech died in the land of Moab some time ago. His wife, Naomi, is selling his land. You are the nearest relative, so you must have the first choice of buying it.'

'Oh yes,' said the relative. 'I will buy the land.'

'If you want the land, then of course you will want to marry the wife of Elimelech's dead son. This is the custom in our country.'

'Oh well, actually I've just remembered that I can't buy the land. I'd like to marry Ruth, of course, but I'm afraid I can't.'

So Boaz bought the land, and he also married Ruth.

In time Ruth and Boaz had a son. And so, even though she had lost her husband and her two sons, Naomi had a family to look after her in her old age. She had someone because Ruth, her daughter-in-law, had been faithful to her.

King David – David is Anointed   (2 min.)

Samuel was an old man. He was the great prophet of the people of Israel and he had obeyed God's will and had chosen Saul as the first king of the Israelites. Saul had defeated all Israel's enemies and was making the land a safe place to live in.

However, instead of following the word of God, Saul was becoming too proud. At last Samuel said, 'It makes me sad to say this, because it was I who chose you to be king, but you are no longer obeying God's will. God will choose a new king in your place.'

When Saul took no notice of this warning, Samuel prayed to God for help.

In Bethlehem was an old man named Jesse. Jesse was a farmer with seven grown-up sons and one young boy. When the great prophet Samuel turned up at the farm, Jesse was amazed. What could he want? Jesse was amazed when Samuel told him that he had come to choose a king of Israel from among his sons. Jesse called his sons to him. As they stood waiting for Samuel to look at them, Jesse felt very proud. They may have been his sons, but they were all fine, upright lads. Samuel called Eliab, the oldest, before him. Jesse was surprised when Samuel said, 'No. This is not him.'

Jesse said, 'But he is tall and strong. He'd make a very good-looking king.'

'God doesn't look at a man's face, nor at the height of his body or the strength of his arm,' said Samuel. 'God looks into his heart.'

Abinadab came forward. It was not to be him. Shammah came forward, but neither was it him. The other young men came forward until all seven stood before Samuel.

'No, it's none of these that God has chosen to be king. Have you no more sons?'

'No,' replied Jesse.

'God told me it would be a son of Jesse of Bethlehem. I can't understand it. Let me see them all again.'

Again the sons of Jesse came before Samuel, but Samuel chose none of them, 'And you have no more sons?'

'Well, of course, I have little David. But David's only a boy. You won't want him. He's far too young to be king of Israel.'

David was brought before Samuel. He had been looking after his father's sheep. As soon as Samuel saw him, he knew that this was the boy who would one day be king of his people. Samuel took out a small bottle of sweet-smelling oil; the oil which was used to anoint the heads of kings. He let a few drops of the oil fall on to the head of the young shepherd boy from Bethlehem.

David and Goliath   (3 min.)

There was war between the Israelites and the Philistines. David was too young to fight in King Saul's army so he went on tending his father's sheep. But he longed to be a soldier just like his three eldest brothers who were fighting with the king.

One day Jesse said to David, 'I want you to take this food to your brothers and then come back and tell me how they are.'

David wasted no time. He reached King Saul's camp just as the two great armies were preparing for battle. There was a buzz of excitement among the troops. When David at last found his brothers they were talking about something that had just happened.

It seemed that the Philistines had a giant in their army, a huge man three metres high by the name of Goliath. Goliath had walked out on to the field in between the Israelite and the Philistine camps: 'I challenge any of you Israelites to come out and fight me,' he shouted. 'If you can beat me, the Philistines will all accept defeat.'

There was silence in the Israelite camp. The Israelites looked across at the man. He was so tall that they would hardly be able to reach up to kill him. Besides, he was covered with heavy armour. Surely it would be certain death to try to fight Goliath.

'You Israelite cowards!' roared Goliath. 'I'll give you time to think about it, and then I'll be back.'

When David heard the story he went straight to King Saul. 'When Goliath challenges the Israelites again,' he said, 'I'll go out and fight him.'

Saul couldn't believe his ears. 'You're only a lad, and this Goliath is a trained fighting man. Besides, he's three metres tall!'

'I have fought lions and bears to protect my father's sheep. And while I sit watching the sheep I practise with my sling and stones. I'll fight the giant. If God looked after me against lions and bears, He'll look after me against the Philistine.'

'If you insist,' said Saul, 'I cannot stop you. May God go with you.'

Saul offered David his helmet, his armour, and his sword. 'I'm afraid I can't use these,' David said. 'I'm not used to them.' And he went to the stream to choose five smooth pebbles. He put them in his shepherd's bag and went forward to meet Goliath.

It was not long before Goliath strode forward again. When he saw David, he burst out laughing. 'Are you going to fight me with your shepherd's crook then?' he roared.

David reached in his bag and took out one of the pebbles. He fitted it in his sling. He whirled the sling round and round his head and let go. The pebble flew through the air too fast to see – and hit Goliath between the eyes. The giant fell dead.

As soon as the Philistines saw this, they turned and ran.

David and Saul   (3 min.)

After David had killed the giant Goliath, King Saul took him home with him and put him in command of some of his soldiers. However, as time went by and Saul heard the people saying what a marvellous fighter this young boy was, Saul began to get jealous of David. Eventually Saul's temper overcame him and in anger he threw a spear at David. It missed and hit the wall. David escaped from the palace in fear of his life and went into hiding.

Saul did not give David any rest while he was hiding. The King decided that he would have to finish him off if people weren't to laugh at him, and he set out to find David.

David had gone to the Cave of Adullum. As the days and months passed, people found out where he was hiding. His father and his brothers brought him food. People who were not happy with Saul as the King of Israel came and joined him, until there was an army of men at the Cave of Adullum. Of course, Saul found out about it too, and started towards it with his army.

One day King Saul had travelled a long way hunting for David. He decided to rest from the hot sun in the shelter of a cool cave. As he lay there asleep, David and some friends came by and found him. David's friends told him that he must kill him now while he had the chance: 'No,' said David, 'he is the King of Israel, chosen by God. I shall not kill him.'

Instead David cut off the bottom of Saul's robe and took it with him. Next day, when King Saul had gone back to his camp, David shouted to him from a safe distance:

'Saul, it was I who cut off the bottom of your robe. I had the chance to kill you, but I let you live. Let me live in peace too.'

Saul realised what wickedness he was doing and was ashamed: 'You're a better man than I am, David,' he shouted back.

That time King Saul went back home. But as time went by he began to feel jealous again. A second time he went hunting for David. This time David stole into his camp while Saul was asleep. Quietly he took Saul's spear and water-flask which lay nearby, although again his men had said he should kill the King. Again David told Saul what he had done and the King was ashamed: 'I am sorry for what I have tried to do,' he said. 'You have rewarded me with good, but I have rewarded you with evil. I know now that you will surely be king, and I will hunt you no more.'

Some time later, just as he was about to lose a battle against the Philistines, King Saul killed himself with his own sword. The leaders of the tribes of Israel chose David to be their second king of Israel. David accepted and not long afterwards captured the city of Jerusalem to make it the capital of his country. But though David was the King of Israel, he always called himself the 'servant of the Lord'.

*

David is said to have written many of the Psalms. Here is the 23rd Psalm:

The Lord is my shepherd; I shall not want.
He maketh me to lie down in green pastures:
He leadeth me beside the still waters.
He restoreth my soul:
He leadeth me in the paths of righteousness for his name's sake.
Yea, though I walk through the valley of the shadow of death,
I will fear no evil: for thou art with me;
Thy rod and thy staff they comfort me.
Thou preparest a table before me in the presence of mine enemies:
Thou anointest my head with oil; my cup runneth over.
Surely goodness and mercy shall follow me all the days of my life:
And I will dwell in the house of the Lord for ever.

(from The Book of Psalms, c.300 BCE; King James Authorized translation of the Bible 1604–1611)

The Fast of the 9th of Av

9th of the month of Av
July/August

Jews fast during the daylight hours to commemorate the destruction of the First and Second Temples in Jerusalem which happened on this day in 586 BCE and 70 CE respectively. The First Temple had been built by King Solomon (c.986–932 BCE) and destroyed almost completely by King Nebuchadrezzar of Babylon (606–562 BCE) in the course of extending his empire westwards from the River Euphrates to the Egyptian border. The Jews were deported to Babylon where they lived in exile until 537 BCE. King Herod the Great (74–34 BCE) rebuilt the Temple on a much more magnificent scale. The great fortress, the Antonia, formed part of the Temple's defences.

This Second Temple became the centre of Jewish pilgrimage and religious activity. During the Roman administration of Palestine it became the political and military centre of Jewish nationalism. After a rebellion the Romans destroyed both the city and the Temple leaving only the western wall, known as the Wailing Wall, standing.

Nebuchadrezzar Destroys Jerusalem   (10 min.)

The prophet Jeremiah stood in the courtyard of Solomon's Temple in Jerusalem and spoke plainly to the priests and the people gathered there:

'These are the words of the Lord: if you do not obey me and do not follow the laws I have given you; if you do not listen to the words of my servants the prophets, whom I have sent to you, but to whom you have never listened, I will destroy this city.'

The Jews were amazed. Everyone knew that King Nebuchadrezzar of Babylon was getting closer and closer to Jerusalem with his army. Was Jeremiah saying that Nebuchadrezzar would destroy Jerusalem? This was treason. Jeremiah must die a traitor's death.

'You're a traitor, Jeremiah!' shouted some of the people.

'Arrest him!' shouted others.

'Put the traitor to death!'

'If you kill me,' answered Jeremiah, 'you will kill an innocent man. The words I speak are not my own. I tell you only what the Lord God has told me.'

People began to argue. Some said that Jeremiah should be executed; but others said that Jeremiah might well be speaking the word of God and they would not risk God's anger by putting him to death. Jeremiah escaped with his life.

Perhaps another man would have kept quiet after this incident, but not Jeremiah. He felt that he had a message from God. He knew he had to tell the people of Judah that they would be destroyed by their own wickedness unless they changed their ways and worshipped the one and only God in the way the Law of Moses commanded them.

Jeremiah continued to preach. Meanwhile King Nebuchadrezzar's army had beaten both the Egyptian and the Assyrian armies. He drew nearer to the land of the Jews. It seemed to Jeremiah that God was using Nebuchadrezzar to punish the Jews for their wickedness.

*

One day Jeremiah stood at the gate of the Temple with a large earthenware jar in his hands. As the people gathered to hear what he had to say, Jeremiah raised the jar above his head and hurled it to the ground where it smashed into pieces.

'The Lord says that he will smash the people of Judah in the same way as a jar is smashed,' shouted the prophet. 'He says the Jews have deserted him. They worship other gods although there is only one God. Just as this jar was smashed to pieces, so Jerusalem will be destroyed.'

This time Jeremiah had gone too far: the governor of the Temple had him arrested. The prophet was flogged and left in the stocks all night long.

Jeremiah realised that he would no longer be able to preach in Jerusalem. It had become too dangerous. However, he could write down what he had heard from God and ask someone else to read it out to the people. Jeremiah dictated the book to his secretary, Baruch. The brave Baruch then took the book and read it aloud to the people coming and going at the Temple gate.

At last the book was taken from Baruch to King Jehoiakim where one of his ministers began to read it to him. When the King had heard the first part he slashed the book with a knife and threw it on to the fire. It was burnt to ashes. King Jehoiakim showed no fear at the prophecy of Jerusalem's destruction. He had heard Jeremiah say the same thing too often. Instead, he ordered Jeremiah's arrest.

However, Jeremiah and Baruch could not be found. They had gone into hiding. There they rewrote the book (which is still to be found in the Bible today and called The Book of Jeremiah).

After King Jehoiakim's death, his young son, also called Jehoiakim, came to the throne. A few months later King Nebuchadrezzar's troops marched into the city of Jerusalem. The young king, Jehoiakim and his family, all his ministers and the officers of the army were all arrested. Together with skilled people from the city; the weapon-makers, the builders and craftsmen, the rich and the clever, they were all taken to the distant land of Babylonia under the watchful eye of King Nebuchadrezzar.

A new king called Zedekiah was placed on the throne by Nebuchadrezzar, because he thought he could trust him. But it was not long before the Egyptian Pharaoh made promises of friendship to King Zedekiah offering him help if he would send troops against Nebuchadrezzar. King Zedekiah sent for Jeremiah to ask him to pray for victory for his army, but Jeremiah could offer no words of encouragement.

'God has decided to use Nebuchadrezzar of Babylon to punish this wicked nation. You cannot win. The best that you can do is to surrender peacefully so that lives will not be lost and men will not be injured in battle.'

Twice Jeremiah was thrown into a dungeon. The second time the dungeon was a deep pit where Jeremiah was starved. But again the King had the prophet released and sent for him to ask his advice and encouragement:

'I can only tell you what I have told you already,' answered Jeremiah. 'If you give yourself up to the King of Babylon, you will be saved, but if you try to escape, you will surely die.'

Even as Jeremiah was set free the armies of King Nebuchadrezzar advanced upon the city. The King did not surrender. The Babylonian army surrounded Jerusalem so that food could not get in and no-one could get out. As food grew short King Zedekiah decided that he wouldn't starve to death and he did not dare surrender as Jeremiah had suggested. He had to escape. Gathering a few faithful soldiers and friends with him, he managed to get through the city gates at night without being seen by the Babylonians. But by morning he was captured. The King of Judah was taken before Nebuchadrezzar who ordered that his eyes should be put out as a punishment; this would make certain that he did not escape again. And Zedekiah was dragged in chains to Babylon.

Meanwhile the Babylonians had broken through the gates of Jerusalem. They plundered the city and burned the palace and the Temple taking with them all the treasures, some of which had been made by King Solomon. These went back to Babylon. The walls of the city were torn down and the houses demolished. All Jews left in Jerusalem were rounded up and taken to join their blind king in Babylon. All that remained in Jerusalem were heaps of smouldering ruins and a few beggars and poor people.

Jeremiah was taken with the Jews who escaped to Egypt although he did not want to go. And somewhere in Egypt, we do not know where and we do not know when, the old prophet died. He had lived through good times and bad, he had preached the word of God when people wanted to listen and when they did not, he had seen the Temple of Solomon repaired and made beautiful, he had seen other gods worshipped in it and children sacrificed in it, and now he had seen the Temple and the city destroyed, as he had always said it would be.

But Jeremiah left a message of hope for the Jews and for all people who sin and wish for forgiveness:

Listen to the word of the Lord, you nations,
and tell it to the furthest islands:
He who scattered Israel shall gather them again
and care for them as a shepherd does his flock.

*

Stop your loud weeping,
And shed no more tears;
You shall be rewarded for your work,
They shall return from the land of the enemy.
There is hope in your future
That your children shall come again to their own country.

(from the Book of Jeremiah, *c*.600 BCE)

The Jews Return from Babylon   (4 min.)

In Babylon the years went by. The Jews were well-treated by Nebuchadrezzar. They were allowed to carry on their jobs and businesses. Many of them settled down so well that they began to forget their homeland. Many too began to forget their religion and began to worship some of the many gods of Babylon. In 539 BCE when King Cyrus of Persia conquered Babylon there were only a few Jews left who were old enough to remember what life had been like in Jerusalem. It came as rather a surprise and shock when the following year King Cyrus announced that the Jews could and should now return home to Jerusalem. Most of the Jews regarded Babylon as their home.

There were a good many Jews, however, who believed that they ought to go back. An advance party, led by King Zerubbabel and the High Priest, Joshua, travelled the thousand kilometres through dangers and desert to Jerusalem. Cyrus gave them some help. He returned treasures stolen from the temple by Nebuchadrezzar sixty years before.

What a shock they had when they reached their city! All of them knew the story of Nebuchadrezzar's destruction of Jerusalem, but when they saw the piles of jumbled stone and the weeds pushing through streets filled with rubble, their eyes filled with tears and their hearts sank. Had they left the comfort of a civilised and wealthy city for this?

The first thing to be done was to build themselves houses for shelter. Then a start was made to clear the city. Not long afterwards Joshua supervised the rebuilding of the altar on the site of the old Temple of King Solomon, but compared with the Temple as it used to be it was a very poor affair, and the people were ashamed to call it their Temple. Many wished that they had stayed in Babylon.

Years went by and the people began to slow down in their building. The city was not the great city it had once been. The people seemed to have no energy to make it so. They began to despair and no work was done on the Temple for fifteen years.

Times became hard. There was drought and famine in the country. Nothing seemed to go right, and people began to wonder why. Then Haggai, a man so old that he could remember the Temple of Solomon before it had been destroyed, claimed to have the answer from God:

'You say that it is not the right time to rebuild the Temple,' he said. 'Is it right that you should live in nice comfortable houses while the house of God has not even got a roof? Are you surprised that there has been no rain and that your crops will not grow?'

Zerubbabel and Joshua realised that God was speaking through Haggai. Work began on the Temple once more.

Some months later a prophet by the name of Zechariah spoke out. He claimed to have had eight visions in which God had shown him what Jerusalem would be like when it was rebuilt. He described the magnificence of the Temple and his visions gave the people the courage and the strength they needed.

There was still much to be done. The Temple was not as magnificent as it had once been. The walls of the city had not been rebuilt and so there was always a danger of attack from enemies. But at last, in the month of March 515 BCE the Temple was finished. A special service was held in which Joshua, the High Priest, offered up thanks and prayers to God.

The prayer that follows is one of the Eighteen Blessings of the Jewish prayer book. It asks God to bring the Jewish people back to their own country.

Sound the trumpet for our freedom,
And raise the flag to gather all the Jews
from the four corners of the earth back to our own land,
Blessed is our God, who gathers together the scattered people of Israel.

(from the Amidah, c.500 BCE)

The misery of the Jews who had been taken to Babylon away from their own country is told in this psalm:

We sat down and wept
By the rivers of Babylon
when we remembered Jerusalem.

We hung our harps on the willow trees,
for those who had carried us off
Ordered us to play and sing;
Our guards told us to be merry:
'Sing us one of your songs' they said;
But how could we sing the Lord's song
In a foreign land?

(from Psalm 137, *c*.300 BCE)

The Romans Destroy Jerusalem   (10 min.)

In the year 64 CE the Roman Emperor appointed Florus to be the Procurator (governor) of Judaea. Florus was a man known for his cruelty and harshness.

In the year 66 CE Florus asked for money from the Temple treasury. The High Priest refused and so Florus sent in his soldiers. The Roman troops marched through Jerusalem to the Temple. As they went through the narrow city streets, they killed anyone who got in their way. They smashed shops and burned houses.

Finally, they entered the Temple and simply took the money that the High Priest had refused to give them.

From their hiding places in the mountains and the desert the zealots gathered together. They were Jews determined to throw the Romans out of their country and govern it for themselves. Secretly they armed themselves and encouraged people to leave the villages to join them. And then in August of that year they struck. They attacked the Roman fortress at Masada, a massive flat-topped rock rising to 50 metres high with steep sides, almost impossible to climb. The Roman garrison was killed and the Jewish zealots took the rock for themselves.

Meanwhile in Jerusalem, the zealots raised the people to anger and to action. In a sudden uprising the people of the city attacked the Roman soldiers who had recently attacked them. They were chased through the city and finally trapped in the palace of Herod where there was nothing for them to do but to surrender.

Orders were sent to the Roman governor of nearby Syria to send reinforcements to help the troops in Jerusalem. The Romans were furious at having been defeated by a handful of Jews and 30,000 extra soldiers were sent from Syria to teach them a lesson. They advanced towards Jerusalem burning every village on the way and killing anyone they could find. They marched on towards the capital of the Jews. They marched up through the mountain pass of Beth-horon little knowing that their march was being watched by a small force of angry Jewish zealots armed and ready for a surprise attack in the narrow pass from which there was no way out. As the 30,000 Romans slowly climbed over the mountain pass the fury of the zealots suddenly swept down on to the Roman troops. Romans were killed by frightened horses, by terrified soldiers trying to escape, and by the swords of the Jews. Although there were far more Romans than Jews, the Romans were in a hopeless position and never really had a chance to fight. The dust rose as the Roman legionaries headed down and away and back to their homes, and when the dust settled there lay 6,000 Roman dead. The zealots had defeated the legion sent to teach them a lesson, they had stolen all their equipment, horses, swords, food, tents, and they had seized the Roman eagle, the standard of the legion. And nothing caused greater shame to a legion than that.

Throughout the land of Judaea the Romans had been driven out and for a short time the Jews ruled their own country.

*

In the year 67 CE the Roman Commander Vespasian arrived with two legions and many auxiliary troops. He was joined by his son, Titus, who brought another legion by sea from Egypt.

By the time the autumn rains came that year nearly all of the land including most of the capital Jerusalem was in Roman hands. And then, on the point of success, Vespasian was called back to Rome; he was to be the next Emperor. He left his son, Titus, to mop up the last resistance in Judaea. Soon, only the Temple area remained in the hands of the Jews.

It was surrounded by Roman troops. Enormous siege engines were rolled into position along the walls, and battering rams hammered away trying to break through. In the Temple the people were in poor condition as food was getting very scarce.

Two giant ramps were built against the Temple wall. These were great towers with platforms at various heights and with ladders leading up to the topmost levels. The Jews tried to attack the engineers working on the ramps, but they knew it would not be long before the Romans came swarming over the walls.

At last the siege platforms rose level with the top of the city wall. At this late stage, Titus promised to spare anybody who surrendered, and some accepted the offer. The Roman General could not bear the thought of the destruction of the Temple which many regarded as the most beautiful building in the world. At last the matter was taken out of his hands. The Roman soldiers, angry and bored with years of waiting, charged into the city and set fire to the doors of the Temple. The whole of the lower city was burned and the entire upper city was pounded to rubble. Hundreds of people were killed. The great Temple of Herod was pulled down stone by stone, so that today nothing can be seen of it at all except for a small part of the western wall. Jerusalem was in ruins.

But that was not quite the end. Johanon and Simon, two of the leaders, escaped with others to Herod's palace and managed to fight the Romans off for another five months before final defeat. Eleazar, the third leader of the Jewish zealots, fled to the rock fortress of Masada. It took the Romans two more years to finish off the zealots here. By building ramps right up to the top of the rock they launched the final attack. The day was the first day of the Jewish Feast of the Passover, the day on which Jews remember how Moses set them free from the slavery of the Egyptians. The two-metre high wall at the top was battered down and the wooden fence behind was burned, but inside the Romans found only the dead bodies of the 960 zealot men, women, and children. All of them had chosen suicide rather than surrender to the Romans.

During the siege of Jerusalem 1,000,000 Jews were killed and 900,000 were captured. Most of the ringleaders were crucified and 700 good-looking young men were taken to Rome to be paraded in the victory march. All men over the age of seventeen were condemned to lifelong slavery in the stone quarries of Egypt, while boys of sixteen and younger were sent to the provinces to be exhibited in the Roman games fighting gladiators or wild animals. Good-looking and healthy boys, girls, and women were sold as slaves, and while they were waiting to be transported 11,000 of them died in prison camps.

In the year 71 CE Titus was back in Rome with the Emperor Vespasian for the great parade celebrating the defeat of the Jews. There were the captured youths in chains led through the streets, there were floats showing scenes from the Roman victory in Jerusalem, and there was Simon, the zealot leader, whose life had been spared so that he might appear in the procession in Rome. Simon was dragged along behind the procession by the neck and whipped all the way. He was then taken to the Tarpeian Rock and hurled down to his death. As a memento of their victory and as a warning to other rebellious people throughout the Empire, the Emperor Vespasian had a special gold coin struck on which were the words – Judaea captured.

And that, it seemed, was the end of the Jews. Today there are about 12,000,000 Jews throughout the world.

*

Jews remember the first time the Temple was destroyed by King Nebuchadrezzar 2,500 years ago, as well as the Roman destruction. In the synagogues The Lamentations of Jeremiah is read. This book was written at the time of the Babylonian conquest:

O Lord,
you are enthroned as king for ever;
your throne lasts from age to age.

Have you quite forgotten us
and left us for so long?
O Lord,
show us the way back to you
and we will come back;
make things as they were for us long ago.
For if you have utterly turned away from us,
then your anger against us must be very great.

(from the Book of Lamentations, *c*.600 BCE)

New Year (Rosh Hashanah)

1st of the month of Tishri
September

The first day of the Jewish year is by tradition the anniversary of the creation of the world from which date the Jewish calendar is reckoned. It will also be the Day of Judgement when God will weigh the good and evil in the souls of individuals after the end of the world to determine their future. The blowing of the ram's horn during the morning service reminds Jews of God's sovereignty over the universe and urges the faithful to be penitent and return to God. The New Year is celebrated for the first two days of the year; these and the subsequent eight days up to the festival of Yom Kippur, the Day of Atonement (q.v.) are days for considering one's behaviour throughout the past year, for asking forgiveness of God, and for harmonising one's relationship with God.

On the first day of the festival the birth of Abraham's son Isaac is recalled; on the second day the story of Abraham's willingness to sacrifice Isaac is told. Abraham who lived in the early second millennium BCE is the patriarch of the Hebrews and the founder of Judaism. Called by God to leave his home town of Ur in Babylonia (modern Iraq), he travelled up the River Euphrates and then south to the land of Canaan (now part of modern Israel). Through his son, Ishmael, whose mother was Hagar, he is the progenitor of the Arab peoples; through Isaac's son, Jacob Israel, whose twelve sons became the leaders of the Twelve Tribes of Israel, he is the father of the Jews. Muslims tell a similar story to that of the sacrifice of Isaac about Ismael (see Id-ul-adha, the Great Festival).

On New Year's Eve apples dipped in honey are eaten. At the morning service in the synagogue the shofar (ram's horn) is blown to recall the sacrifice of the ram by Abraham.

Abraham Prepares to Sacrifice Isaac   (2 min.)

The prophet Abraham, the father of the Jews, was a hundred years old when his wife bore him a son. Sarah and Abraham laughed with joy when the boy was born and they named him 'Isaac' which means Laughter.

One day Abraham had a message from God. God told Abraham to take Isaac to the top of the hill and there he must sacrifice his son to God. Abraham dearly loved Isaac, but after all God had given the boy to him; if God wanted the boy back, then Abraham had to give him.

The next morning early, Abraham put the saddle on his donkey and set out with his son and with two of his men. They travelled for three days until Abraham saw the mountain where he knew God wanted him to make his sacrifice.

'Stay here with the donkey,' Abraham told the two men, 'and when Isaac and I have worshipped God, we will came back to you.'

Abraham took the wood to burn the sacrifice and loaded it up on to Isaac's shoulder. He took the knife and the fire and together they set off up the mountain.

'Father?' said Isaac.

'What is it, son?' asked Abraham.

'We have got the fire and the knife and the wood, but where is the young animal for the sacrifice?'

'Don't worry, son; God will make sure we have something to offer to him,' replied Abraham.

Father and son continued to the top of the mountain. When they were there Abraham set up an altar with some large stones that were around the place and then he began to lay the wood around the altar, for once the sacrifice had been killed, it was then burnt as an offering to the Lord. Isaac watched, unable to understand where the sacrifice was to come from.

When his father began to tie his hands and feet, he understood what God had asked Abraham to do. He did not struggle or fight, but let his father tie him securely and then lay on the wood on top of the altar.

Abraham raised the knife ready to kill his only son. He raised the knife, but before he could bring it down, he heard a voice from heaven. The Angel of the Lord spoke:

'Do not kill the boy. Do not harm him. God is satisfied that you were prepared to give your only son and he is well pleased with you.'

Abraham thankfully put down the knife. He looked up. Not far away from the altar was a clump of bushes. Entangled in the bushes by his horns was a fine ram. As Abraham untied Isaac and helped him down from the altar, he said: 'God has given us something to offer up to him, my son.'

Gratefully the two untangled the ram and offered it as a sacrifice to God. Abraham and Isaac came down from the mountain and returned home. Abraham loved his only son more than anything else he had – but he loved his God most of all and had proved that he would do anything for him.

*

We can't all be as strong in our faith as Abraham was. This Jewish prayer asks God to forgive us for our sins (New Year is a time when Jews think of their failings in the past year and decide they will try to do better in future):

Forgive us, our Father, for we have sinned;
Pardon us, our King, for we have done wrong;
For you are the God of goodness, the God of forgiveness.
Blessed is our God, who is gracious and forgiving.

(from the Amidah, *c.*500 BCE)

The Day of Atonement (Yom Kippur)

10th of the month of Tishri
September/October

The Day of Atonement is the culmination of the first ten days of the year which are spent considering how far from God's wishes his people have strayed and how God's forgiveness is needed to see the people through the coming year. This most solemn of Jewish holy days is marked by a fast which begins on the evening of the previous day and ends at dusk of the day itself. No food or drink is taken by all over 13 for 25 hours. Synagogue services are marked by the white dress worn by the officiants and the white drapes over the reading desk and Ark of the Covenant, the cupboard containing the Scriptures; white symbolizes the purity to which the faithful aspire.

Before the Roman destruction of the Temple in 70 CE the High Priest entered the Holy of Holies, the sacred inner sanctum which was not otherwise entered, to confess his own sins and those of his nation and to ask for absolution from God. The final service of the day ends with the sounding of the ram's horn, the shofar, previously heard during the New Year's morning service. This reminds Jews that the self-examination of the past ten days should lead them to continue through the year as they resolved at the beginning of it.

God's mercy on a truly repentant people is illustrated by the reading from the Book of Jonah, a prophet of the 8th century BCE, who was called by God to preach his message to the wicked city of Nineveh in Assyria (modern Iraq). Believing Jonah's warning of divine destruction and reforming their evil ways saved the city from God's anger.

Jonah and the Whale   (3 min.)

Jonah heard the word of God telling him to go to the city of Nineveh and tell the people how angry God was with them for their wickedness. Jonah lived in the land of Judah, a small country that had been conquered by the mighty Assyrian Empire. Nineveh was the capital of this empire. The people there were rich and well-educated even if they were wicked; why should they listen to Jonah, a foreigner, from a tiny far-off country who couldn't even speak their language properly? Jonah didn't take long to decide that he was not going to Nineveh.

Jonah reached the sea-port of Joppa where he intended to cross the Mediterranean to Tarshish. In a foreign country he thought he would be able to get away from his God, for he thought God lived only in the land of Judah. Jonah paid his fare and got on board the ship.

The ship sailed away from Judah in the opposite direction from Nineveh. Jonah was not shy about telling the sailors and the other passengers on board why he was going to Tarshish – he was escaping from his God who had a job for him to do that he definitely did not want to do. He was going to a country where his God could not reach him. Having spoken to several people on board, Jonah went to get some rest in a corner of the boat. As he lay in a deep sleep the weather worsened. A hurricane began to blow and the waves threw themselves high above the ship. The sea lashed the ship so hard that the captain became worried that the boat would break up. He ordered the crew to throw heavy things overboard to lighten the load and help keep them afloat better.

Jonah still lay sleeping as each sailor called out to the god of his own country for help. They thought that if they all prayed to their own gods, one of the gods might hear. The captain came and woke Jonah. 'Are you still asleep?' he shouted. 'Get up and pray to *your* god, and perhaps he might save us!'

The sailors talked amongst each other, and at length decided that someone on board must have brought bad luck to them all. They decided that it must be Jonah; after all Jonah himself had told them that he was running away from his god.

'What shall we do with you?' said one of the sailors to Jonah. 'The storm's getting worse all the time. We've got to do something.'

'Throw me overboard,' replied Jonah bravely. 'I know it's my fault, all this bad weather. Throw me into the sea and the waves will go down.'

But the sailors were not so hard-hearted. They started to row towards the nearest land so that Jonah could be left there; but the sea became so rough and the wind blew so hard that the rowers could make no headway at all.

'Oh God,' cried the sailors. 'We will have to throw this man into the sea to save the passengers and ourselves. Do not think of us as murderers. This storm is your storm and this man is running away from you.'

So Jonah was thrown into the sea. Gradually the wind died down and the sea became calm once more. The ship and everyone on board continued safely to Tarshish.

Meanwhile Jonah managed to keep himself afloat for some time. Suddenly there was a great movement in the sea. As the waters thrashed about, Jonah realised that a great fish was splashing around near the surface and getting nearer to him. Desperately be began to swim the other way, but with a few flips of its enormous tail the biggest fish that Jonah had ever seen moved closer to him. Opening its huge jaws, it swallowed Jonah in one mighty gulp and he was swept down into the stomach of the monster.

For three days and three nights Jonah stayed alive inside the great fish. While he was there in the darkness he prayed to God: 'Oh God, it is my own fault that I have ended up here, but you have saved me from the sea. Save me now to do your work. Other men may forget their gods, but I shall believe in my God from now on. You may be sure of that.'

And so three days after the fish had swallowed Jonah, it spat him out on to dry land. Once again God commanded Jonah to go to Nineveh, and this time he obeyed at once.

Jonah in Nineveh   (3 min.)

Jonah heard God's message telling him to go to the wicked city of Nineveh to tell the people of God's anger with them.

Jonah had been to great cities in his own land, but they were like tiny villages compared with the city of Nineveh, capital of the Assyrian Empire. The walls around the city were tall and strong. The buildings inside were so huge and magnificent that Jonah felt very small indeed. He thought that the whole of Jerusalem would probably fit inside one of the enormous buildings. Everywhere were statues of strange-looking gods. The streets were thronged with rich people going about their business. Many people had slaves with them. Jonah began to wish that he had stayed at home, but he remembered that he had promised God he would do his work.

He set off for the centre of the city where he planned to talk to the people. The city was so big that he had to walk through wide streets and between tall buildings for a whole day before he reached the centre – the marketplace – where he could speak to as many people as possible.

To Jonah's amazement, he was not laughed at. He was not stoned, nor was he arrested or killed. Instead, people listened to him. With God's help, he spoke so well that everyone crowded round to hear him and blocked the marketplace where he stood. As the days passed and the news of Jonah's message spread through the great city, the people began to realise how wicked their ways had been. Many truly felt sorry and ashamed.

At last it came to the King's ears that a Jewish prophet was preaching the message of God in the city. Even he understood. Orders went out from the royal palace that all the inhabitants of Nineveh should fast and should beg forgiveness from God for their sins.

God heard their prayers and did not destroy the city, but forgave the people because they were really sorry for the way they had lived.

But Jonah was angry. He had not wanted the people to be forgiven by God but to be destroyed for their wickedness. Anyway, wasn't God his God, the God of the Jews and not of foreigners? Jonah went out of the city and sat under the shade of a tree which God had grown especially for him to sit under. As he sat there brooding he felt glad of the tree's cooling shade, for the sun was very hot. The next day Jonah still sat there being cross with God when he noticed that the tree was withering. The leaves fell off until there was no shade from the burning sun for him.

Jonah was angry because he had no shade, but he felt sorry for the dying tree. Then God spoke to Jonah:

'You are sorry for the tree?'

'Yes Lord. I am sorry. It lived such a short time. I wish I were dead, too.'

Then God spoke gently to him. 'You are sorry for this tree, which you neither planted nor watered. How much more sorry I would have been to destroy the people of Nineveh? Should I not be sorry for those hundred and twenty thousand souls? And should I not forgive them, whether they know me or not?'

*

At the Day of Atonement synagogue service the famous prayer, the Shema, is repeated, as it is at most other services. If one prayer could be said to hold within it the heart of the Jewish religion, this is it.

Hear, O Israel:
the Lord our God is one God;
And you shall love the Lord your God with all your heart,
and with all your soul, and with all your might.
You shall hold the words I teach you in your heart,
you shall teach them carefully to your children,
you shall say them when you sit at home,
and when you walk down the street,
and when you go to bed and when you get up.
I am the Lord your God,
who brought you out of the land of Egypt,
to be your God;
I am the Lord your God.

(from the Shema prayer in the Book of Deuteronomy, *c*.800 BCE)

The Feast of Tabernacles (Succot)

15th of the month of Tishri
September/October

*In the Bible, this is described as an eight-day festival. The early rabbis (priests)
added an extra day which is still retained by Orthodox Jews though no longer
held by the Progressive. It ends with The Rejoicing of the Law (q.v.) and is
associated with the living in tabernacles (temporary huts) after the escape of the
Israelites under the leadership of the prophet Moses from slavery in Egypt under
1400 BCE (see the Feast of the Passover). This used to be one of the festivals at
which Jews made pilgrimage to the Temple in Jerusalem before its destruction in
70 CE. Many Jews erect tabernacles in their gardens for the duration of the
festival and either live in them or carry out their religious obligations in them.
Synagogue services entail the singing of Psalms 113–118 and the carrying, in
procession, of palm branches. On the seventh day the branches are carried seven
times round the synagogue and prayers of salvation are offered. The festival is
associated with harvest. On the last day prayers are said for rain and for good
crops.*

Moses and the Israelites in the Desert   (5 min.)

After many years of slavery in Egypt, God spoke to Moses and told him to set his people free. Moses went to Pharaoh, the Egyptian King, and told him that God would send down upon the land of Egypt terrible plagues if he refused to let the slaves go. Pharaoh took no notice.

Finally God sent the most dreadful punishment of all – the death of the eldest son of each family. Moses told the Israelites to mark their doors with the blood of a lamb or a kid. They should cook and eat the lamb and then go to bed for the night. The Israelites did as Moses said. At midnight that same night God sent the Angel of Death to the Egyptians and the firstborn son of every house in Egypt was found dead. Not one of the Israelites was touched. The Angel of Death had passed over their houses.

After this, Pharaoh told Moses to take his people and go straight away.

Once the Israelites had left, taking their sheep and cattle, Pharaoh began to feel vengeful. He prepared his army to set out after them. The chariots soon caught up with the Israelites, trapping them against the shores of the Red Sea. Then Moses went to the edge of the water. A strong wind began to blow. The gale blew stronger until the waters of the sea parted and were soon shallow enough to walk through. Moses walked forward across the gap in the waters and the Israelites followed. The Egyptian army arrived as the last of the Israelites crossed to the other side in safety. The charioteers watched in amazement.

Then Pharaoh roared, 'What are you waiting for? After them!'

Fearfully the Egyptian soldiers drove forward. As they came to the middle of the Red Sea where the waters had parted, the wind suddenly dropped. With a mighty roar the water rushed back and Pharaoh and his army were drowned.

The people were delighted to have escaped the hard work and cruelty of Egypt. They set out to find the land that Moses said had been promised to them by God. However, the courage of many people failed them and, as soon as things were hard, they began to complain and wish they had not left Egypt.

From the Red Sea Moses led his people on through the desert. Soon they ran out of water and there was none to be found. Then they found a pool at Marah, but as soon as the first man had tasted the water it was realised why the place was called Marah, which meant 'bitter' – the water was bitter and undrinkable.

The people began to complain bitterly.

'You've brought us into the desert where there is no water,' they grumbled, 'and, when at last we find water, we can't drink it. What are we supposed to do?'

With God's help Moses found a branch. He threw it into the water and the water gradually cleared. He tasted it and the water was sweet. And the people drank.

Moses led the Israelites further into the desert. Food became very scarce. Again some of the people started to complain: 'Things may have been hard in Egypt, but at least we always had something to eat. We're all going to die of starvation in this desert. What are we supposed to do now, Moses?'

Again God told Moses what to do. He promised to give the Israelites meat for their evening meal and bread for the morning. This would happen every day for a week.

And that night a flock of quails settled all over the camp. Quails are birds about the size of pigeons. Having crossed the sea on their migration, they landed exhausted in the desert. The people of Israel found them easy to catch and eat. The next morning the ground was covered with white flakes.

The Israelites collected as much as they could to take back to their tents. They called it manna and did not know what it was; a white juice drips from the tamarisk tree which dries into white flakes and can be eaten. God had provided both food and drink for the people.

For forty years the Israelites wandered through the hot dry desert where very little grew and where there was scarcely shade or shelter. With Moses to guide them and God to lead him, they never went short of food or water. And at last they came to the promised land, the land now called Israel.

*

The gathering in of the harvest is associated with the Feast of Tabernacles. The Jews believe they have a covenant with God. This is a sort of a bargain that if they worship and believe in him, he will look after them through good times and bad.

If you listen carefully to the commandments I give you,
To love the Lord your God,
And to serve him with all your heart and with all your soul,
I will give you rain on your land at the right time of year,
the early rain and the late rain,
that you may gather in your corn and your wine and your oil.
And I will give you grass in the fields for your cattle,
and you can eat and be full.

(from the Shema prayer in the Book of Deuteronomy, c.800 BCE)

The Rejoicing of the Law (Simchat Torah)

23rd of the month of Tishri
October

This festival is the final day of the Feast of the Tabernacles (q.v.) and an occasion of great happiness. Joyful hymns are sung. The children are blessed, and given sweets, fruit and flags. A joyful procession, carrying the scrolls of the Law, goes seven times round the synagogue. During the synagogue service the first and last chapters of the Law are read.

The Law book is known as the Torah or Pentateuch (the Five Books). It consists of the Books of Genesis, Exodus, Leviticus, Numbers, and Deuteronomy and has a central place in the Jewish religion. The first chapter of the Book of Genesis gives an account of the creation of the universe. The last chapters of the Book of Deuteronomy give the last words of the prophet Moses to his people and tell of his death.

The Death of Moses   (5 min.)

Moses had been called by God to lead the Israelites from their slavery in Egypt to a land where they could settle down and live. The land would be flowing with streams that never dried up. Springs of sweet fresh water would run from the hills. There would be rich pasture for the cattle and blossom for the bees; and the land would flow with milk and honey. Farmers would be able to grow wheat and barley, figs and pomegranates, olives and grapes, and there would be iron and copper mines.

For forty years now Moses had led the people of Israel around the hot, dry Arabian desert searching for this Promised Land. For forty years Moses had to put up with the groans and moans of the faint-hearted Israelites. Whenever they ran short of food or water they began to complain and wish that they'd never left Egypt; but for forty years Moses had always been told by God where to find food and water and the people had survived.

More recently the danger had come from fierce tribes who would ride down from the mountains and try to steal the Israelites' possessions. Or they had to pass through lands belonging to tribes who did not want them to cross their country.

On the journey Moses received messages from God telling him to teach his people how to behave towards God and towards each other. This is what God commanded Moses to say:

'Hear, O Israel, the Lord is our God, one Lord, and you must love the Lord your God with all your heart and soul and strength. These commandments which I give you this day are to be kept in your heart; you shall repeat them to your sons, and speak of them indoors and out of doors, when you lie down and when you rise.'

And the Israelites came to the land of Moab. The western border of the land was the River Jordan; on the other side of the River Jordan lay the land of Canaan, the Promised Land. At this time Moses was a hundred and twenty years old, and although his sight was as good as ever and he was still very fit, he knew that the time was very near when he must die. Moses made camp with the people of Israel for the last time and spent the time writing down the laws that God had given to his people. He called Joshua, the leader of the fighting men, to him. Joshua had seen the Israelites safely through enemy territory many times.

'Joshua, be strong, be determined for you shall bring the Israelites into the Promised Land,' said Moses.

Then Moses called the priests to him, and said, 'I have written down the words of God. Keep them in the Holy Tent. Make sure that you and the people follow the laws that God gave to me for you.'

Last of all Moses called all the people of Israel to him, and said, 'God has told me that my end is near. He has told me that, although I shall never cross the River Jordan into the land he has promised, he will take me to a high place. There I may see the land where you and your children will live. I ask you to remember the laws I have given you through God. They are not just empty words; they are your very life, and you shall live by them in the land across the Jordan.'

Moses left his people and was taken by God to the top of Mount Nebo from where the old prophet could see the whole of the Promised Land before him. He could see rivers and hills and valleys, fields and farms and towns and in the far distance he could see the shining Mediterranean Sea. And there, in sight of the Promised Land, the man who had brought the children of Israel to freedom was taken up into God's Kingdom.

*

The last chapters of the Book of Deuteronomy are read in synagogues on the day of the Rejoicing of the Law. Just before he died, Moses set out very clearly to the Israelites the choice they had to make:

Today I offer you the choice of life and good, or death and evil. If you obey the commandments of the Lord your God which I give to you, if you love the Lord your God and follow his commandments and laws, then you will live and God will bless the promised land you are about to enter. But if you turn your hearts away and you do not listen and you bow down to other gods and worship them, I tell you that you will die, you will not live long in the promised land. I offer you the choice of life or death, of blessing or curse. Choose life and then you and your children and their children will live; love the Lord your God, obey him and hold fast to him: that is life for you in the land which the Lord promised to give to your forefathers. (from the Book of Deuteronomy in the Torah, c.900 BCE)

The Festival of Lights (Hanukkah)

25th of the month of Kislev
December/January

King Antiochus IV of Syria (born c.215 BCE, ruled c.175–163 BCE), self-styled Epiphanes meaning God-manifest, attempted the Hellenisation of his kingdom whose boundaries roughly corresponded with the empire of the Babylonian King Nebuchadrezzar. His policy throughout his lands, including the Jewish home-land, was that the Olympian Zeus should be worshipped in the same style as in Greece, Antiochus's dynasty having been founded by one of the generals of Alexander the Great of Macedon on the break-up of the latter's empire.

Greek statues were placed in the Jewish Temple in Jerusalem, where Jewish priests clad in Greek clothes with Greek-style hair carried out the Olympian rituals to the gods of Greece. Naked Jewish boys competed in athletic games in the Temple courtyards and Jewish representatives were sent to Pagan festivals and games throughout the kingdom. Most Jews accepted the King's orders without outward complaint, but the desecration of the Temple in 167 BCE precipitated the revolt led by Judah the Maccabee (or Judas Maccabaeus, i.e. Judas the Hammer), who drove out the King's troops and rededicated the Temple three years later to the day. Although the Jews were beaten by superior forces at Betzechariah in 163 BCE, Syrian dynastic problems caused the general to withdraw and grant the Jews their traditional religious freedom. Judas Maccabaeus insisted on gaining political freedom for the country and was killed in battle at Alasa in 161 BCE.

The feast is celebrated for eight days in commemoration of the one jar of oil found by the Maccabees before the rededication of the Temple, which was expected to keep the candelabrum alight for one day but which lasted for eight. In Jewish homes and synagogues one candle is lit on the first night, an additional one on the second, and so on, until the eighth night, when all eight candles burn on the candelabrum. Psalms 113–118 are read during services held on this week.

The festival was established by Judas Maccabaeus in 164 BCE as an annual reminder to Jews everywhere of the constant struggle which they must make to preserve their religion against weakening influences.

Judas Maccabaeus Restores the Temple   (7 min.)

Antiochus IV was the King of Syria. At his command all the small countries that he had conquered had to stop worshipping their own gods in their own ways and worship his gods. The land of Judah was one of the countries conquered by this powerful and cruel man.

Soldiers brought orders from King Antiochus that the Jews should stop praying to their one God and worship the king of the Greek gods, Zeus, and the other gods in which Antiochus believed. Most of the Jews did as they were told and worshipped the gods of Antiochus in the synagogues and not the one God. Not all Jews did this. There were some who could see that the Jews were breaking the laws that God had given to Moses, but what could they do with so many against them?

The face of Israel was changing. People started to wear the Greek-style clothes of Antiochus. Statues were placed in the synagogues where the Jewish priests now looked like Greek priests. In the Temple at Jerusalem, built by King Solomon, were statues to the Greek gods. Sacrifices were made to them. And Jews were not even allowed to go to the Temple on the Sabbath (Saturday), their holy day.

In the year 169 BCE Antiochus went to fight against the Romans in Egypt hoping to make his empire larger. The message came back to Jerusalem that he had been killed. Immediately the High Priest and others began to clear the Temple of Greek things. The statues were taken to the Temple city walls and thrown over, where they smashed to pieces on the rocks some thirty metres below. Priests who worshipped the Greek gods were also flung over the walls. The city was made a Jewish city once more.

In Egypt Antiochus was roundly beaten by the Romans. He was furious at this defeat. He was even more angry when he learned that people believed he had been killed. And when he heard that the tiny country of Judaea had rebelled against him, his rage was terrible. From Egypt, Antiochus marched his men back to Jerusalem to find some way of taking revenge. The soldiers killed everyone they met. They searched the houses and murdered the occupants. Young and old, men, women, and children all suffered the anger of King Antiochus of Syria. After three days nearly ten thousand people had either died or been sold into slavery.

Antiochus had new statues put up in the Temple. He had new priests appointed to pray to his gods. He gave Jewish homes and lands to foreigners, persuading them to come to live in Jerusalem, where he hoped there would be less trouble with them than with the Jews. Before he left the city he ordered the Temple to give up its treasure and its money. When this was refused he marched in and took it himself.

In 167 BCE Antiochus sent one of his officers to dedicate the Temple to the god Zeus and to make sure the Jews were following his orders. The holy altar of the Lord had a statue of the Greek god Zeus placed upon it and pigs were burned there as sacrifices. (As the pig is believed by Jews to be an unclean animal, this was a terrible thing to happen). This occurred on the 25th day of the Jewish month of Kislev.

Not all the Jews did as the Syrian king commanded. In the village of Modin a priest by the name of Mattathias was ordered by a Greek officer to pray to the god Zeus:

'You're an important man here,' said the officer, 'if you follow the King's orders, everyone else will, and you will be handsomely rewarded.'

'My sons and I will follow the ways of our fathers. We will never obey the commands of the King.'

As Mattathias spoke a Jew from the village came forward to the altar and began to offer a sacrifice to the Greek god. Unable to control his fury Mattathias rushed up with his sword drawn and killed the man where he stood. Then he turned and killed the King's officer.

Mattathias called his five sons to him. The one named Judas Maccabaeus he appointed as their leader. Together they went to gather faithful Jews into an army to drive out the Syrians from Judaea. They secretly entered the towns and villages to get support. Soon they had an army of six thousand men. They attacked any town or city offering up sacrifices to the Greek gods and not to the One God. They attacked the strongholds of Syrian soldiers. Twice they attacked the forces of King Antiochus sent against them and twice they won.

The King now ordered General Lysias to take 50,000 of his army and attack Judas Maccabaeus. Judas gathered his troops ready for the battle. 'There are far more of the enemy than there are of us,' he cried. 'But remember that it is better to die fighting than to live to see our land taken.'

During the night Lysias sent a contingent of his men to sneak up on Judas's camp and kill them all while they lay asleep. Judas had found out about this and when the Syrians got there the camp was deserted. The message went back to Lysias that the Jews had run away. However, when dawn broke, the army of the Maccabees had gathered and was in position to fight the Syrians.

Again Judas spoke to his men, 'Do not be afraid because we are outnumbered. Pray that God will be with us and do your best.'

Suddenly the Maccabaean army charged. The Syrians retreated in confusion. When the other Syrians saw the main part of their army fleeing, they too began to run away. Those who were not killed by the Jews fled.

The next year Lysias gathered a huge force of men to attack Judaea. He was so confident of winning a great victory that he had sent out notices to all the slave merchants telling them what prices he would charge for the captured Jews. Once again Judas Maccabaeus and his small desperate army were victorious and once again Lysias had to retreat to his own land.

Most of the land of Judaea was now free. Judas marched in triumph towards the capital, Jerusalem. Proudly Judas Maccabaeus entered the Temple. It was the 25th day of the month of Kislev in the year 614 BCE, exactly three years after Antiochus had first desecrated the holy Temple. Now a special service was held. The Temple had been cleansed. The foreign statues had been removed and the Jewish priests were dressed in their own Jewish costume. Candles were lit all around the Temple and the whole place was filled with praise and with singing and music. Then the Temple was rededicated to God. By the altar was a great oil-lamp. In the Temple only one jar of pure oil had been left untouched by the Syrians. It was enough to keep the altar lamp burning for just one day. The lamp was lit and it continued to burn for the eight days of the Festival of Rededication.

*

Here are the words of a hymn whch is sung at the festival of Hanukkah:

O God,
You are like a castle on a high rock,
A place of safety;
And it is only right to praise you.
Let the Temple be made clean and pure again
And I will offer you there my thanks;
Let the slaughter and swearing in the Temple be stopped
And I will sing and praise you at the blessing of the altar.

(from the Maoz Tsur hymn – Rock of Ages)

Muslim Festivals

New Year (The First of Muharram)

1st of the month of Muharram

This is the Muslim festival of the New Year, Muharram being the first month of the Muslim year. The Muslim era dates from the Hijra, the emigration of Muhammad and his followers from his birthplace, Mecca, to Medina about 340 km to the north, to avoid persecution in 622 CE. A religious community was set up under Muhammad's leadership. At this festival Muslims attend communal worship at the mosque, tell stories of the Hijra and usually take the day as a holiday.

Muhammad's Flight from Mecca   (6 min.)

When the Prophet Muhammad began preaching the message of his new religion in the Arabian city of Mecca, there were many people who did not want to hear. Muhammad taught that there are not many gods but only one God, Allah; this upset the guardians of the temple (the Ka'ba). He taught that women were equal to men, in a country where wives belonged to their husbands and where baby girls were thought of as worthless and sometimes buried alive. Muhammad and his wife set free all their slaves at a time when most slaves were treated with great cruelty. And they gave away most of their money to help the poor and the sick.

One day Muhammad was walking in Mecca when a camel suddenly escaped from its master and charged down the narrow street. Camels are big animals and can be very fierce. They have strong teeth and a powerful kick. Everyone in the crowded street panicked and dashed for safety in doorways. But Muhammad had often travelled with camels through the desert and knew just how to handle them. He went to the angry beast, soothed and calmed it

156

and led it back to its owner. The man was very pleased and thanked Muhammad, but the Prophet had some harsh words for him:

'A camel doesn't run away if it's looked after and fed properly. Feed him and keep him well and your camel will work hard for you.'

The man was shocked to hear these words, but he realised the truth of what Muhammad had said.

Every day as Muhammad walked down the street in Mecca, a woman who was sweeping out the house would brush the dust at him. But every day Muhammad would cheerfully greet her with 'Assalamu Alaikum' (which means 'Peace be with you'). She would give no answer and would slam the door.

One day Muhammad came down the street expecting to be covered with dust as usual, but the door of the house was shut and the woman wasn't there. Muhammad asked the neighbours where she was and, although they were surprised that he should want to know, they told him that she was ill in bed. Immediately the Prophet went into the woman's house, made her a meal, fetched the water from the well, tidied up, and even swept the dust from the floor. She was amazed and ashamed that he should take such care of her when she had shown such hatred for him, but Muhammad came every day until she was better again.

The woman became one of Muhammad's followers, and whenever he saw her afterwards and said 'Assalamu Alaikum' she always replied 'Wa Alaikum salam' (And Peace be with you).

*

As the number of Muslims in Mecca grew, the people who made money from the temple began to stir up hatred against them and there were even attempts to kill Muhammad. Eventually he decided to leave and go to Yathrib where there were already some Muslims. The people here welcomed him hoping he would bring peace to their troubled town, and he did. He built the first Muslim mosque there for prayer and worship, and the number of followers grew rapidly. Although there was peace in the city of Yathrib there was much fighting between them and the people of Mecca.

Muhammad was at Yathrib for eight years and the city changed its name from Yathrib to Medina-al-Nabi (Medina for short), meaning the City of the Prophet. He now marched on Mecca with 10,000 Muslim followers. There was no fighting – Mecca surrendered. There was no revenge, no robbery or looting, no damage to houses, and nobody was harmed. Muhammad stood before the Meccans in the temple where more than 300 statues to different gods were kept, and asked them:

'What do you think I should do to you now?' They hung their heads shamefully, remembering that they had driven the Muslims out of their city. But Muhammad said:

'Go. You are free.' He ordered his followers to destroy all the statues in the temple and said that this particular temple, the Ka'ba, was the special holy place of God. All Muslims try to visit it once during their lives.

Muhammad died and was buried at Medina two years later, but the number of Muslims continued to grow. Now, after about 1,400 years, there are perhaps 800,000,000 Muslims across the world in North Africa, Pakistan, Turkey, Iran, Jordan, Arabia, Iraq, Afghanistan, Indonesia, Sudan, Syria, India, and in many other countries including Britain.

*

Praise be to God,
All things in heaven and on earth belong to him;
To Him be praise for evermore;
He is full of wisdom and He knows all things.
He knows all that goes into the earth
And all that comes out of it;
He knows all that comes down from the sky
And all that goes up to it.
God is most merciful and forgiving.

(from Sura 34 of the Qur'an, *c*.610 CE)

*

In the Name of God, most Gracious, Most Merciful.

By the glorious morning light
And by the night when it is still,
Your guardian Lord has not forgotten you
Nor is he displeased.
The future will certainly be better for you than the present,
And your guardian Lord will give you something which will make you well
    pleased.

Did He not find you as an orphan
    and give you shelter and care?
Did He not find you lost and guide you?
Did He not find you in need
    and take your need away?
So don't treat the orphan badly;
And don't turn away the beggar;
But tell everyone of the goodness of the Lord.

(from Sura 93 of the Qur'an, *c*.610 CE)

The Tenth of Muharram

10th of the month of Muharram

The majority of Muslims are Sunnis (from Arabic Sunna – the way) and follow the tradition of sayings and deeds of Muhammad as well as the Qur'an. Sunni Muslims predominate in North Africa, Pakistan, Turkey, Jordan, Saudi Arabia, Afghanistan, Indonesia, Sudan, and Syria with sizeable minorities in many other countries. The Shi'a sect split from the mainstream in 679 CE. Shi'ites constitute about 15% of Muslims, being found mainly in Iran (where Shi'ism is the state religion), Iraq (about 50%), with minorities in India and some Arab countries. There are about 50 million Shi'a Muslims compared with 750 million Sunnis.

The split occurred over the succession after the death of Muhammad in 632 CE. Muhammad was the founder of a religion and an empire which needed leadership. Abu Bakr, a faithful friend of the Prophet became caliph (successor) after Muhammad's death, followed in succession by Umar Uthman who was murdered at the age of eighty, and Ali, the Prophet's son-in-law and cousin, who was also murdered in 661 CE. The Syrian governor, Mu'awiya proclaimed himself caliph, as did Ali's son, Hassan. Hassan had no ambitions and soon resigned, being succeeded in his claim by his brother, Hussain, who reasserted himself after Mu'awiya's death. Shi'ite Muslims acknowledge Ali and his sons as the rightful successors of Muhammad and call the line of leaders descending from Ali, the Imams (leaders).

Hussain died on the tenth of Muharram at the hands of Mu'awiya's son, Yazid, and the day is celebrated by Shi'ites in passion plays, processions of mourning, the flying of black flags, and even self-inflicted flagellation.

The Death of Hussain   (7 min.)

All religions stress that they are ways for people to live peacefully together. But very often arguments and even wars break out because people cannot agree. Not many years after the Prophet Muhammad died, the Islamic religion was split by serious quarrelling as to who should be the leader of the Muslims. The father of a man named Yazeed had been the last caliph, so Yazeed was made caliph when his father died. However, another man named Hussain was also proclaimed caliph. His father had been Muhammad's own cousin and had married Muhammad's daughter, so many people thought he was the right man.

It was Dhu-al-Hijja, the last month of the Muslim year when many Muslims travel to Mecca to worship God at the Ka'ba. Hussain had also come to the city as a pilgrim but it was not long before he discovered that not everybody in Mecca had gone there to pray. Thirty men had been paid by Yazeed to kill Hussain, who did not want any fighting in the holy city so he quietly left Mecca with his friends.

Hussain set out for a town called Zarood. He never reached it. Long before he was near the town he saw the desert sand raised to a cloud of dust by many men. When they came into sight Hussain realised they were the men of Yazeed's army. The commander of the soldiers was General Hur. He spoke respectfully to Hussain, telling him that he need not fear for his life but that he must come as a prisoner to the town of Kufa. Hussain refused and set off again. General Hur's soldiers followed. Hussain stopped; the soldiers stopped. Hussain marched on quickly; so did the soldiers. Everywhere that Hussain went, General Hur's men followed.

The date was the first of Muharram – New Year's Day.

One of Hussain's friends came to him:

'Let's attack them now, suddenly. We'll surprise them and maybe we'll win. But if we wait Yazeed will probably send a bigger army.'

Hussain refused. He would not be the first to shed blood.

On the second of Muharram, Hussain stopped his men and said that he would go no further. They all looked and saw nothing, just the open desert near Karbala. Hussain felt perhaps that this was the place where he was to die.

During the next few days the governor of the town of Kufa sent soldiers against Hussain. Hussain had about 70 men who watched from their camp as the number of his enemies grew. At last there were 4,000 soldiers standing against them. Hussain was running out of water. The situation was getting desperate.

On the ninth of Muharram, Hussain realised that he would at last have to fight. He spoke to his men:

'We're trapped here at Karbala. We're 70 against 4,000, so there's little chance of success. If you choose to leave me, and surrender to the enemy, I will not hold it against you. Go now if you wish.'

Nobody moved. They had all decided to stand by Hussain even if it meant death.

Meanwhile, in the enemy camp General Hur, who had been following Hussain for the past week-and-a-half, was talking to the Governor of Kufa.

'You're not going to attack Hussain, are you, Governor?'

'But, of course, General. Either he gives up – or he dies.'

General Hur thought deeply about this. He had followed Hussain and his small band of followers for so long that he had come to respect them. They were few against many. If they didn't give up, they would all surely die. Yet none of them had surrendered. None seemed to be afraid. General Hur went to his brother and to his son and talked quietly to them. As night fell they decided to quietly leave the camp and join Hussain.

Hussain welcomed his old enemy and as the soldiers slept Hussain and the General knelt down to pass the night in prayer.

Morning broke on the tenth of Muharram. It was not long before the enemy began to shower the small camp with arrows. Most of the arrows fell on Hussain's tent. Hussain rode bravely out to speak to the enemy soldiers, but the Governor of Kufa refused to talk and Hussain was forced to retreat.

From morning until evening the seventy fought on. As the sun set, the battle came to an end. All of Hussain's men were dead – General Hur, his brother and son, all the soldiers, the women, Hussain's baby son, and Hussain himself. On the tenth of Muharram, exactly forty years after the Prophet Muhammad's death, his grandson Hussain died for his beliefs.

Today not all Muslims believe that Hussain should have been the head of the Islamic empire. Those who do, especially remember the tenth of Muharram. They perform plays about his death and great processions are held, particularly in Iran. However, all Muslims respect Hussain's death and remember it on this day.

*

People who have given their lives for God are called martyrs. They are venerated in Islam and are mentioned in the Qur'an.

God gives you life and He gives you death;
And God sees very well all that you do.
If you are killed or die for God,
Forgiveness and mercy from God are far better
Than all the wealth an unbeliever can collect.
If you die or are killed for God
You are brought together in God.

(from Sura 3 of the Qur'an, c.625 CE)

Prophet's Day (Meelad al-Nabi)

12th of the month of Rabi' al-Awwal

Muhammad was born in Mecca, Saudi Arabia, about 570 CE and died on the same day in the Muslim calendar in 632 CE. His birthday is of prime importance for Muslims for whom Muhammad is the most important of a long line of prophets including Moses, Abraham, Joseph, David, and Jesus. The day (and the month) are celebrated by special assemblies and the telling of stories of the birth and life of the Prophet to the young. Mecca was a growing commercial city on an important trade route, but strong links remained with the desert heritage. City dwellers often sent their children, as part of their education, to spend time with desert nomads. There were Jewish and Christian communities in the vicinity but the city was famed for the shrine of the Ka'ba (literally the Cube) around which shrines to many tribal and local deities were placed. Much money was made in Mecca as it was a centre of pilgrimage. Before Muhammad's time Allah (God) was worshipped by the Arabs as the creator and superior god – but many other gods were also worshipped.

The Birth and Early Life of Muhammad   (8 min.)

Mecca is a city in the Arabian desert where, nearly 1,500 years ago, there lived the merchant, Abdullah, with his wife, Amina. Abdullah was worried – there had been a long drought, the wells were running dry and there was no sign of rain. People were hungry and many were ill including Abdullah himself. Worse still, Amina was expecting a baby any day, and Abdullah had to go away on business. Abdullah set out across the desert in the burning heat and soon afterwards he died. A few days later his son was born. As Amina nursed her new child she began to hear the heavy patter of raindrops on the dusty ground outside and, as the shower became a heavy storm, she heard the cheerful shouting and cheering of people dancing around in the rain. Amina took this as a sign that her son Muhammad was to be someone special.

Until he was six Muhammad spent his time with a tribe of wandering Arab shepherds in the desert. Soon after he returned home his mother died. He lived with his grandfather until he was eight and when the old man also died Muhammad was taken into the care of his uncle Abu Talib, a merchant and the head of Muhammad's tribe.

Muhammad's time in the desert had taught him how to care for sheep and now he became his uncle's shepherd. He was so trustworthy that other people asked him to look after their sheep too and the money they gave him helped to pay for his keep. After a sad beginning things began to look better for Muhammad.

As he grew older Muhammad began to travel with the camel trains his uncle took to far-off lands. Sometimes they went to Palestine or Syria (over 1,500 kilometres away) where he would hear Jewish and Christian stories. With each trip his uncle would let Muhammad do more and more important jobs and eventually Muhammad became the leader of a camel caravan. All the merchants knew they could trust him with their goods and their money.

Once, when Muhammad had been on a trading expedition he arrived back in Mecca to learn that there had been a terrible flood. The waters had swept through the open-air temple and knocked down the wall that had the sacred Black Stone built into it. The wall had been built up again but no-one could decide who should have the important job of putting the stone back in place. Finally an agreement was reached that the first man to come into the Ka'ba would be asked for his solution to the problem. In came Muhammad. The people asked him what to do. He spread his cloak on the ground and put the Black Stone on to it.

'All of you take hold of the cloak,' said Muhammad, 'and you will all have the honour of carrying the stone.' When they reached the place Muhammad himself put the stone back so there could be no more argument. Everyone said what a wise decision he had made.

A rich widow in Mecca had heard of Muhammad's wisdom and honesty and asked him to look after her affairs. They got on so well that after a short time Muhammad and Khadijah got married. Although she was rich the couple gave away most of their money to the sick and the poor and they set free all of Khadijah's slaves. Although the poor were very grateful, most of the people in Mecca thought Muhammad had gone mad.

*

Muhammad cared for all people, especially the poor. Once, when a rich old woman died, her son came to Muhammad to ask what sort of monument he should build to her memory. Muhammad told him to dig a well, so that whenever the poor went to fetch water they would remember and bless his mother's name.

*

On one occasion Muhammad was talking to the chief of a tribe, a very important man. A poor blind man recognised Muhammad's voice and interrupted them to ask about God. Muhammad was angry and turned away from the blind man. But as he carried on speaking to the rich chief he suddenly grew ashamed. He realised that all men should be treated fairly whether rich or poor, sighted or blind.

*

Muhammad was hated by some people in Mecca. He taught that it was wrong to worship many gods in the Ka'ba and that there was only one God (Allah). The people who worshipped at the Ka'ba and the traders who made money out of the pilgrims who prayed there thought Muhammad was a mischief-maker. When Muhammad and Khadijah gave away their money to the poor and set free their slaves, perhaps many people in Mecca felt guilty, and they hated him. There were some attempts to kill Muhammad but none of them succeeded.

On one occasion Muhammad was travelling with a camel caravan. It was midday, when the desert sun is high in the sky and at its hottest, so everyone was resting in the shade of some trees. Muhammad fell asleep. He was awakened by a shout. Standing over him was a man with a sword.

'Who can save you now?' shouted the man.

'God, Almighty Allah will save me,' said Muhammad, and calmly got to his feet. The man was so surprised and shocked that he dropped his sword. He had expected Muhammad to be frightened of death. Muhammad snatched up the sword, pushed the man against the tree and held the sword to his throat:

'And who can save *you* now?' asked Muhammad.

'Only you can save me,' said the terrified man.

'Be merciful then,' said Muhammad and let him go. The man became a Muslim and followed the teachings of Muhammad for the rest of his life.

*

Muhammad told the people about the word of God in the Holy Qur'an. Here is part of its meaning in English:

Goodness is nothing to do with whether you face east or west to pray. The good man is the one who believes in God, in the angels, in the Scriptures and in the prophets; the one who gives his money to his family, to orphans, to the needy, to travellers, to beggars, and for freeing captives, for the love of God; the good man is the one who says his prayers when he should and gives his money to charity; who is true to his promises; who is strong in trouble and danger and times of war. These are the true believers, the ones who fear God.

(from Sura 2 of the Qur'an, *c.*625 CE)

Here is the meaning in English of the call to prayer. It is always recited in Arabic, the language Muhammad spoke, and calls Muslims to prayer five times a day, every day of the year.

God is greatest.
I testify that there is no god but God
 and that Muhammad is His Prophet.
Up to prayer,
Up to salvation,
Prayer is better than sleep.
God is greatest.
There is no god but God.

The Month of Ramadan and the Night of Power (Lailat al-Qadr)

(usually 27th Ramadan)

The Small Festival (Eid-ul-Fitr)

1st Shawal

All healthy Muslims over the age of twelve spend the daylight hours of Ramadan abstaining from food and drink and other pleasures. Fasting is the fourth of the Five Pillars of Islam laid down by God in the Qur'an, the others being: 1 – recitation of the Kalimah or Creed (la ilaha illa Allah: Muhammadun rasulu Allah – There is no god but God and Muhammad is His Prophet), 2 – the five times daily ritual of prayer, 3 – the giving of alms to the poor, and 5 – pilgrimage to Mecca. Fasting teaches control of body and mind, it enables well-fed people to appreciate the plight of the poor and is a unifying factor of the Muslim faith.

The Night of Power (Lailat al-Qadr) is celebrated on one of the odd-numbered nights during the last ten days of the month of Ramadan and commemorates God's first revelation through the Archangel Gabriel to Muhammad. Part of the night is usually spent in prayer and reading the Qur'an.

The end of Ramadan comes when the new moon is sighted (thus the month may last 29 or 30 days) and the Small Festival, prescribed by Muhammad, takes place on 1st Shawal. No work is done on this day and prayers are said congregationally at the mosque. Traditional meals of celebration are eaten, presents are given to children, and greetings cards are sent wishing 'Eid Mubarak' – Happy Eid. In Muslim countries the holiday lasts for three days, though in the United Kingdom just one day's holiday may be observed. This is the most popularly celebrated Muslim festival.

Muhammad is Given the Holy Qur'an   (3 min.)

While he was still a young man, Muhammad's honesty and truthfulness became well known to all in Mecca, including a rich widow who asked Muhammad to look after her business affairs. They got on so well together that soon Muhammad and the widow Khadijah were married. Although they were very rich, they gave away most of their money to the sick and poor and they set free all of Khadijah's slaves.

Muhammad now began to spend more and more time thinking about religion. He would go to a cave in a hillside overlooking the desert. In the darkness of the cave it was cool and quiet, a place where he could sit and think. Muhammad thought about the people of Mecca, worshipping their many different gods, and he began to understand that there is really only one God. Muhammad used the name 'Allah' which is Arabic for 'the God'.

For some years Muhammad meditated in the cave, when one day, during his fortieth year, the Angel Gabriel appeared before him. Gabriel called Muhammad the Messenger of God. He then spoke to Muhammad and commanded him to repeat what he had said until he knew it by heart.

The angel vanished and the Prophet rushed home to his wife to tell her what had happened. Khadijah told him that he had received the word of God.

Many times after that Muhammad went back to the cave where the Angel Gabriel gave him the messages of God. Muhammad learned what was told him and repeated the words to his wife and to the people of Mecca.

This was the beginning of the Muslim holy book. It is known as the *Holy Qur'an*, a word that means something that has been spoken by heart.

In the Qur'an Muhammad repeated the things God said to him through the Angel Gabriel. Muhammad was unable to read or write, and Gabriel ordered him to recite God's messages until he had them by heart. Then the Prophet recited the words of God to friends of his who wrote them down for us.

Muslims believe the Holy Qur'an to be the actual word of God which was first spoken in Arabic and so really cannot be translated into any other language properly. So when you hear the Qur'an read in any language other than Arabic you are only hearing part of the meaning and not all of the true word of God. This is why Muslims always say the Qur'an in Arabic, even though they may not understand the language. Of course, every true Muslim will try to learn Arabic so that he will be able to really understand his holy book and be a better Muslim.

*

These are the first words revealed to Muhammad by the Angel Gabriel:

Recite,
In the name of the Lord
Who created man from a drop of blood.
Recite,
For your Lord is most generous;
He taught man to read and write,
And He taught man what he did not know.

(from Sura 96 of the Qur'an, *c.*610 CE)

*

And here the Prophet Muhammad describes the Night of Power when the Qur'an was revealed to him.

We have revealed
This message
In the Night of Power;

And how can you understand
What the Night of Power is?

The Night of Power
Is better than a thousand months.

Then the Angel Gabriel
Came down
From God
With God's Message.

Peace
Until the rising of the morning.

(from Sura 97 of the Qur'an, *c.*620 CE)

The Great Festival (Eid-ul-Adha)
10th of the month of Dhu-al-Hijja

This festival and Eid-ul-Fit, the Small Festival, are the two feasts prescribed by Muhammad himself. Dhu-al-Hijja is the last month of the Islamic lunar year and the one during which, at least once in a lifetime, a pilgrimage to Mecca should be made by all who can afford it. This should take place from the 8th to the 13th of the month. On the 10th of the month Muslims remember that Ibrahim (Abraham) was prepared to sacrifice his son Ishmael (the Old Testament says it was Isaac) at God's command. God intervened and Ibrahim was given a ram to sacrifice instead. At Mecca, and throughout the world, Muslims may sacrifice a sheep or goat to remind them that they too should be prepared to give anything to Allah. Arab tradition identifies the place as Mina, a few kilometres north of Mecca and holds the Ka'ba at Mecca to have been built by Ibrahim in commemoration. (Jews believe Abraham's proposed sacrifice of his son to have occurred on the site of the Temple of Jerusalem, a position now occupied by a mosque called the Dome of the Rock.)

Living at some time during the second millennium BCE the biblical Abraham led his tribe from Ur of the Chaldees in Babylonia (now Iraq), up the River Euphrates to Haran (on the border of modern Syria and Turkey) and south to Canaan (Israel). Abraham and an Egyptian woman, Hagar, were the parents of Ishmael whose twelve sons became the leaders of the Twelve Bedouin Tribes of the Desert, the Arabs; Abraham and Sarah were the parents of Isaac whose son, Jacob or Israel, by four wives, was father to the leaders of the Twelve Tribes of Israel, the Jews.

Despite the festival's name, this is not such a great popular occasion as Eid-ul-Fitr, the Small Festival (q.v.).

Ibrahim Prepares to Sacrifice his Son   (6 min.)

Many years before Muhammad's time there lived a man called Ibrahim. Ibrahim was the leader of a small tribe of Hebrews, shepherds, and cattle-breeders who travelled around the Middle East searching out places to feed and water their animals and moving from town to town to sell them. Muhammad knew God by the name Allah, but in those days Ibr him's tribe thought his name was so holy that no-one should speak it. They called him by the consonants in his name which were YHWH, (Yahweh), sometimes called in English Jehovah. Of all the people of the desert, and of all the people of the cities and towns, Ibrahim's tribe was unusual in that they worshipped only one God. Most worshipped many different gods; a town or tribe may have had their own special god, but they believed that there was many others as well. The Hebrews believed that there was only one God, Jehovah.

Ibrahim travelled many hundreds of miles with his people. He believed that God was leading the Hebrews to a land where they would live in peace and become a great nation. Ibrahim passed through dry hot deserts and stayed near large cities where many different gods were worshipped; sometimes the journey was hard and some of the tribe argued; sometimes the towns where they camped attacked them and they were forced to move on. Eventually the Hebrews came to the land of Palestine and there they stayed for some time.

On one occasion Ibrahim took his son Ishmael and wife Hagar on a journey to Mecca. Ibrahim had returned home. Hagar was desperately looking for water for her young son after their hot and tiring trek through the desert. She began to panic and ran from place to place but could find no water. She sat down, exhausted, to rest. And as she sat her small boy kissed the bare rock. Immediately a spring of pure fresh water burst out and they were able to quench their thirst.

Muslims on pilgrimage to Mecca run between the hills Safa and Marwa to remember Hagar looking for water. And they drink at the well of Zamzam which was later built around the spring.

While Ishmael and his mother were at Mecca, Ibrahim once again set out on the long journey across the desert to join them. While he was with Ishmael at Mecca Ibrahim had strange dreams. On his travels Ibrahim had been shocked to see that some of the peoples he met sacrificed children to their gods. The Hebrews would sacrifice a sheep or a lamb to their God, but how could anyone give up a child for a sacrifice? But at Mecca Ibrahim had a dream in which God asked him to sacrifice his own son Ishmael. Ibrahim knew he dare not question the will of God.

Ibrahim told Ishmael what God commanded. 'Do what you must,' said Ishmael. 'We must both do as God wants.'

Together Ishmael and his father went up to a wild and lonely place in the mountains behind Mecca. Here they built an altar of stone and prepared a fire of branches and twigs. With grief in his heart Ibrahim laid his son on the altar and raised his knife to sacrifice to God.

But, before Ibrahim's hand could fall, God spoke to him. God was well pleased with Ibrahim's obedience. Ibrahim had been prepared to sacrifice anything for God. But God did not take human sacrifices. Turning round, Ibrahim saw an angel holding a ram for sacrifice instead of Ishmael. After the sacrifice father and son, Ibrahim and Ishmael, went back happily together to Mecca.

Together they built the Ka'ba, a huge cube-shaped building which Muslims call 'the House of God'. In it Ibrahim placed a stone, believed to have fallen from heaven. Since Muhammad's time all Muslims try to visit the Ka'ba in Mecca once in their lives.

While they are there some kiss the Black Stone – as many thousands of pilgrims to Mecca have over the years. Then the pilgrims from countries all over the world walk seven times round the Ka'ba. The pilgrimage should be finished by the tenth day of the last month of the Islamic year, 10th Dhu-al-Hijja. On this day Muslims remember Ibrahim's willingness to sacrifice his son Ishmael. Sacrifices of sheep or goats are made throughout the world, but especially at Mecca. Often the meat of the lamb is used for a great feast, or it may be given to the poor. The Eid-ul-Adha, the Great Festival, is a happy time when everyone enjoys themselves – but Muslims also remember the serious meaning of the day.

*

This prayer begins the Qur'an and is repeated many times by Muslims who pray five times a day:

In the name of God, most gracious, most merciful.

Praise be to God,
The Lord of the worlds,
Most gracious, most merciful;
Ruler of the Day of Judgement,
We worship you
And ask for your help.
Show us the straight way,
The way of those you have favoured,
Not the way of those who have made you angry,
Nor of those who have wandered away.

(from Sura 1 of the Qur'an)

*

This is from the final chapter of the Qur'an:

In the name of God, most gracious, most merciful.

I seek safety with the Lord of men,
The King of men, the Judge of men,
From the evil whisperings
In the hearts of men.

(from Sura 114 of the Qur'an, c.610 CE)

Sikh Festivals

The Birthday of Guru Gobind Singh

January

After the martyrdom of Guru Tegh Bahadur (q.v.), on the orders of the Mughal Emperor of India in 1675, his nine-year-old son, Gobind Rai, became the tenth leader of the Sikhs. Gobind Singh (1666– 1708 CE), as he was later known, set the style of the Sikh community for future years. He set up the Khalsa (Punjabi, the Pure), the brotherhood of Sikhs, each equal in the sight of God and sworn to wear the symbols known as the Five Ks: kesh – uncut and unshaven hair, kangha – a comb, kirpan – a short sword for self-defence, kara – a steel bangle whose shape is a reminder that God has no beginning or end, and kachha – shorts originally worn for ease of movement in battle but also worn as a symbol of chastity. Guru Gobind Singh also forbade the smoking of tobacco, the taking of drugs, and the drinking of alcohol. He commanded all Sikh men to add the name Singh (Lion) to their surname and women to add Kaur (Prince) to emphasise the equality of the sexes in Sikhism (see New Year –Baisakhi). Gobind Singh discontinued the line of human gurus and vested all authority in the collection of writings by previous gurus and others, the Granth Sahib (Holy Book), henceforward to be known as the Guru Granth Sahib.

Gobind Rai Becomes the Last Sikh Guru   (3 min.)

On the borders of India and Pakistan is the Punjab, the Land of Five Rivers. It was here, about 500 years ago, that Guru Nanak founded the Sikh religion. The religion grew quietly, getting stronger year by year as more and more people became Sikhs. At first the Muslim emperors of India took little notice, but as the years went by and still more people became Sikhs, they began to get worried that the sect was becoming too powerful.

And the emperors began to take action. The fifth guru, Arjan Dev, was

171

tortured to death by the Emperor's men. The sixth guru, Hargobind was involved in a number of battles with the Emperor's troops and spent some time in the Emperor's prison. Later, the ninth guru, Tegh Bahadur, was also arrested and thrown into prison in Delhi. When the Emperor ordered him to stop being a Sikh, Guru Tegh Bahadur refused, and was beheaded.

After the Guru's death some faithful Sikhs managed to carry his head back to his son in the hills. The new guru was Gobind Rai – but he was only nine years old. As he grew older he realised that the Sikhs would often have to fight so that they could follow their beliefs. He gathered all Sikhs together into something like a Church and an army and asked all Sikh men to add the name Singh to the end of their own names, and all Sikh women to add the name Kaur. Singh means 'lion', Kaur means 'prince' – everyone would now be able to tell who was a Sikh and who was not.

Soon after Gobind Singh had formed his army the soldiers of the Emperor attacked them. The Sikhs were very determined and many fierce battles took place. A large number of Sikhs were killed, but the Emperor never managed to beat them. It seemed that as more Sikhs were killed, the rest grew stronger. In the end the Emperor had to give up, and left them in peace.

Guru Gobind Singh and the Water Carrier   (2 min.)

During one of the battles between the Emperor of India's soldiers and the Sikhs some of the Sikh guards brought a prisoner to the tent of Guru Gobind Singh. But the man was not one of the Muslim soldiers of the Indian Emperor. Gobind Singh could see by his turban and beard that he was one of his own Sikhs. The Guru asked why the man had been brought before him.

'He is a traitor,' came the reply. 'He has been helping the enemy!'

The Guru asked for an explanation from the man, and the prisoner, whose name was Ghanava, answered:

'I am a water-carrier. When the battle is raging or when the armies rest, it is my job to take water round to the wounded and dying, to the tired and thirsty. Today the battle has been fought under the hot glare of the sun and I ran around the battlefield backwards and forwards to give our men water. As the fighting stopped for the day I hurried around the dying and injured soldiers with water for their dry lips.'

'This is true,' shouted the guards, 'but he was giving water to our Sikhs *and* to the Emperor's Muslim soldiers as well.'

'Is this true?' asked the Guru.

'It is quite true,' said Ghanava. 'When I was walking round the scene of battle, I saw no Muslims and I saw no Sikhs; I could only see your face in every man who needed help.'

'You are a true Sikh,' said the Guru, and ordered that Ghanava should be given ointment so that he could help heal the wounds of the injured soldiers. From that day the water-healer Ghanava was called Bhai Ghanava. Bhai means brother and it is a title given only to very special people. Bhai Ghanava was a special man who held all men and women to be his brothers and sisters.

Guru Gobind Singh Finds a True Sikh   (1 min.)

Nowadays all Sikh temples (gurdwaras), have a kitchen. Here the Sikhs eat together to show their belief that all men and women are equal. People may be tall or short, thin or fat, rich or poor, men or women, but in the sight of God all are equal. It was the very first Sikh guru, Guru Nanak, who taught this.

Guru Gobind Singh taught the same thing, and he decided that all Sikh households in the city of Anandpur should have an open kitchen to provide food for anyone who might need it, especially travellers, and pilgrims on religious journeys. One day the Guru decided to test his Sikhs so he disguised himself as a pilgrim and went into the streets very early indeed.

At the first houses he visited there was no reply. The people were still in bed. A little later, and sleepy voices told him to go away because the householders weren't up yet. Later still and they told him to go away because they hadn't even started cooking and so of course there was no food. Nowhere was Guru Gobind Singh offered the free food that Sikhs should provide for travellers.

Nowhere, until he came to the house of a Sikh called Bhai Nandlal. Nandlal gladly showed him into his house and talked kindly to him. He sat him down at the table with a cheerful smile and set a place for him to eat. A few minutes later, Nandlal brought in some steaming dishes of half-cooked meat, half-cooked vegetables, half-baked bread, and uncooked rice.

'Nothing is really cooked yet,' said Bhai Nandlal, 'but you're very welcome to eat now or wait until the meal is ready.'

The next day Guru Gobind Singh told everyone that there was only one real Sikh kitchen in the city of Anandpur – that of Bhai Nandlal.

The Sikh Holy Book   (3 min.)

The Sikhs have a Holy Book. It is a collection of hymns, prayers, poems, and sayings by many of the Sikh gurus including the very first, Guru Nanak, and some by Muslim and Hindu saints. Before the death of Guru Gobind Singh it was simply called the Granth Sahib – the Holy Book. Now it is called the Guru Granth Sahib, because Gobind Singh declared that there would be no more human gurus after his death. Instead the Holy Book, the Granth Sahib, would be the guru.

Only ten men have been gurus and to this day the only guru the Sikhs have is the Granth Sahib. In every Sikh temple (gurdwara) there is a copy of the Granth Sahib. Sikhs bow to it when they come into the gurdwara and then sit cross-legged on the floor so that they are lower down than the book. This is a sign that the Book is greater than anyone, no matter how rich or famous or powerful, because in it are the words of God as spoken by the gurus. If the book is to be carried anywhere it has to be higher than the people and so it is carried on the head. Some Sikhs read it every day, and it is read all the way through (the reading lasts two full days and nights) on very special occasions.

*

Here is part of the Guru Granth Sahib. Many Sikhs know this by heart and say it every morning. It was written by the first guru, Guru Nanak.

There is one and only one God,
Within our hearts, yet beyond the universe;
His name is Truth
And he made all things;
He fears nothing and nothing is his enemy;
He lives for ever and was made of himself;
Thanks to the Guru, He was made known to us;
He was Truth in the beginning,
He was true throughout the ages,
He is true now
And he shall be true for ever.

(from the Japji, Guru Granth Sahib, c.1500 CE)

*

Gobind Singh believed all men to be equal and wrote:

All men are the same although they appear different.
The light and the dark, the ugly and the beautiful,
The Hindus and the Muslims have developed differently
because of their different surroundings;
All human beings have the same eyes, the same ears,
The same body built of earth, air, fire and water.
The names of Allah and Abhekh are for the same God;
The Hindu and Muslim Holy Books talk about the same thing.
All human beings are the reflection of one and the same God.
Recognise the whole human race as one.

Hola Mohalla

late February or March

The spring full moon fertility festival of Holi is celebrated in Northern and Central India and is the occasion of wild festivities and childish pranks including the throwing of coloured powder or water (and sometimes oil, mud or paint) over passers-by. The tenth guru Gobind Singh changed its significance for Sikhs by initiating a three-day festival known as Hola Mohalla which begins on the eve of Holi and is far more subdued, being a time for serious talks and discussions about the Sikh religion. Dating from the original military manoeuvres that were practised at the time of Mughal persecution of the Sikhs, sporting competitions and demonstrations of horsemanship take place.

As there is no Sikh story attached to Hola Mohalla there follows an important episode of Sikh history, that of Maharajah Ranjit Singh and the Sikh state of the Punjab.

After the death of the tenth guru, Gobind Singh in 1708 CE, the Mughal Emperor of India tried to destroy the Sikhs completely: it was a time of great persecution. However, in 1747 the King of Afghanistan invaded India through the Khyber Pass, defeating the Mughal armies. The Mughals lost the Punjab and the Sikhs drove out the Afghans. There followed a time of civil war until the leader of one of the twelve Sikh tribes, one Ranjit Singh (1780–1839 CE) gained control of the Punjab (and later of Kashmir), capturing the capital Lahore in 1799 and taking the title Maharajah (Great King) of the Punjab in 1800.

Maharajah Ranjit Singh   (4 min.)

For many years after the death of Guru Gobind Singh, the tenth and last human guru who had made the Sikhs an army of warrior-saints, the Indian Emperor tried to destroy the Sikh religion. Many Sikhs died for their beliefs and many had to leave their homes to find safety in the wild places and hills of the Punjab. Eventually the Indian Emperor was defeated by the Afghans and the Sikhs had the Punjab to themselves. But the twelve Sikh leaders could not agree amongst themselves and Sikh began to fight against Sikh. One leader proved to be more powerful than all the rest – his name was Ranjit Singh.

Ranjit Singh was a small ugly man – smallpox had marked his face badly and he had only one eye, but he was a very strong leader and a good Sikh. In the year 1800 he became the Maharajah (or Emperor) of all the Punjab.

Maharajah Ranjit Singh lived in a magnificent palace in Lahore, which is now in Pakistan. Then it was the capital of the Punjab. All around were signs of his power and riches – everywhere were smart Sikh soldiers carrying modern guns, and great cannons guarded the city. The palace Ranjit Singh lived in was large and beautiful, the walls were of finest marble decorated with wonderful carvings. The people of the court were dressed in expensive silks and wore jewels and gold. But Maharajah Ranjit Singh dressed only in plain white clothes, although he was the maharajah of the strongest country in all India.

Ranjit Singh gave a lot of money to build new gurdwaras (Sikh temples) and to improve old ones. The most famous gurdwara in the world at Amritsar was built nearly 300 years ago by the fifth guru, Arjan Dev. It is of white marble and is in the middle of a man-made lake. Ranjit Singh paid for the gurdwara to be made bigger and had nearly all of the outside of the temple covered with gold. It is now known as the Golden Temple. Sikhs from all over the world travel to worship there and see the gold of the temple reflected in the blue waters of the lake.

When Ranjit Singh was Maharajah of the Punjab, the British invaded and conquered most of India. While Ranjit Singh was alive he had an army of 80,000 well-trained Sikhs carrying modern weapons. The British did not dare to attack the Punjab. However, in 1839, after ruling the Punjab for 40 years, Ranjit Singh died and there was much argument among the Sikhs as to who should be the next maharajah. The British took their chance and attacked. After this First Sikh War of 1846 part of the Punjab became British. Two years later the Second Sikh War took place. Although the British suffered badly at first, they fought back and eventually conquered the whole of the Punjab.

The new maharajah, Duleep Singh, was only a child and he was captured and sent to England. He lived in a very large house in the small village of Elveden in Suffolk until his death. If you go there today you can see, rising above the tiny English cottages and surrounded by English woodland, the beautiful Indian palace where he lived. Duleep Singh gave a lot of money to the church – not to a Sikh gurdwara, because there were none in England then – but to the little Christian church of St. Andrew and St. Patrick. In its graveyard you can still see the tomb of the maharajah and his wife.

*

As a king trying to lead a simple life, Maharajah Ranjit Singh must have known this Sikh prayer:

If I were a king on a throne with an army
With power and taxation all mine,
It would be worthless if I had these things
But forgot God and his holy name.
(from the Japji, Guru Granth Sahib, c.1500 CE)

New Year (Baisakhi)

13 or 14 April

Baisakhi was originally a New Year celebration for some Hindus. Amar Das, the third guru (1479–1574 CE) instituted this as one of the two annual Sikh gatherings (the other being Diwali in November), Baisakhi is now celebrated as the anniversary of the founding of the Khalsa, the religious society of Sikhs by the tenth guru, Gobind Singh (1666–1708 CE). Sikh baptismal ceremonies are carried out on this day. They still follow the pattern of the original one in 1699. In the Punjab, fairs and celebrations take place and the traditional dancing of one man on top of an upturned pot on another's head. (See also Guru Gobind Singh's Birthday.)

The Founding of the Army of Soldier-Saints   (5 min.)

For many years the emperors of India tried to put an end to the Sikh religion. Some of the Sikh gurus were executed. Now the tenth guru, Gobind Rai, decided that he must join all Sikhs together so that they would be strong in the face of the enemy. The great Sikh festival of Baisakhi was soon to be held. Gobind Rai sent messages to all the villages throughout the Punjab telling as many Sikhs as possible to travel to the town of Anandpur for the festival.

On the day of Baisakhi many thousands of Sikh men and women gathered in front of a closed tent. It was said that Guru Gobind Rai was inside. As the crowd grew bigger, the waiting people wondered why they had been called together. After some time the door of the tent opened and Guru Gobind Rai stepped forward. In his hand he held a long curved sword sharpened on both sides. It was the *khanda*, the destroyer, the Sikh weapon of war. The crowd fell silent. Everyone listened expectantly. When every eye was on him, Gobind Rai spoke.

'You are all faithful Sikhs, otherwise you would not be here now. I want one of you to prove your faith to me.' He held up his sword, 'Which one of you has faith enough to give me his head?'

There was not a sound. No-one moved. No-one spoke. Everyone was shocked and amazed. Had they really heard him right? Would he really kill a Sikh to show how faithful he was? Everyone wanted to prove himself, but no-one wanted to die. Still no-one moved and not a sound was heard. At last one man moved forward towards the Guru's tent. Sword in hand the Guru led the man inside and the door closed. Seconds later there was a thud and the Guru came out – his sword was smeared with blood.

The crowd could hardly believe it. Nor could they believe it when they heard the Guru ask for the head of a second loyal Sikh. Some of the crowd muttered angrily and turned and left. But another brave Sikh stepped forward and was taken into the tent. Again there was a thud and again the Guru came out holding his blood-stained sword for all to see.

The same thing happened once more. Altogether the Guru asked for the heads of five Sikhs. Five times the sword fell and five times the sword was stained with blood. The last time the Guru came back out of the tent, he pulled open the door – the crowd saw that inside were the five Sikhs, alive and smiling – and the beheaded bodies of five dead goats. Gobind Rai brought out the five brave men – two from the upper classes, a rich landowner and a noble knight, and three from the lower class. He called them the first five members of his new brotherhood. He had asked for their heads to see who were brave enough to give their lives for him. He wanted an army of men and women to be soldier-saints strong enough to overcome any enemy.

Finally, the Guru mixed up a special sweet water called amrit, which he stirred with his sword, then he sprinkled it over the five men. He asked them to do the same to him to show that although he was the Guru, all men were equal before the One God. Then the people were given amrit to drink as a sign of their renewed faith. The Guru made rules for Sikhs to live by and to remind them that they are Sikhs. Sikhs must not shave or cut their hair. They should wear a steel bracelet. They should not smoke or drink alcohol. Gobind Rai asked all Sikh men to add Singh (which means 'lion') to their own name, and all Sikh women to add Kaur (which means 'prince'). This was to remind them of their religion and to show everyone else that they were Sikhs. Many Sikhs keep these rules today.

The festival of Baisakhi is the Sikh New Year festival. Sikhs remember Guru Gobind Rai (or Gobind Singh as he is now called) and this is the time when adult Sikhs are baptised to become full members of the Sikh church, like the first brave five at Baisakhi nearly 300 years ago.

*

Guru Gobind Singh wrote a book of hymns and poems. Here is a verse which shows how all people and all things belong to God:

Sparks rise up from a fire
And spread out in all directions,
But in the end they fall on the earth from which they came.

Dust floats up from the earth
And spreads out in all directions
But in the end it falls back on that same earth from which it came.

Waves rise up from the sea but fall back into the same sea;
So do all things, living or not,
Come from God
And in the end
Return to God.

The Martyrdom of Guru Arjan Dev

May/June

Guru Arjan Dev (1563–1606 CE) was the fifth Sikh guru at the time when the Mughal rulers of India were beginning to fear the increasing number and power of the Sikhs. Guru Arjan collected the Sikh scripture, the Granth Sahib (the Holy Book) which is now recognised by Sikhs as the living Guru. He began the building of the Sikhs' central shrine, the Golden Temple in Amritsar, India (although it was only later gilded by Maharajah Ranjit Singh). Guru Arjan was executed on the orders of Emperor Jehangir.

Guru Arjan Builds the Golden Temple   (2 min.)

Arjan's father, Guru Ram Das, founded the city of Amritsar in the Punjab which has since always been the holiest city in the world for Sikh men and women. It was at Amritsar that Guru Arjan decided to build a gurdwara (a temple). It is now the best-known of Sikh gurdwaras and is called the Golden Temple. The gurdwara was built in the middle of a man-made lake. Many Sikhs expected to see a tall, imposing building. It would impress people and show them what a great religion was that of the Sikhs. But Guru Arjan had other ideas.

'We Sikhs do not need a tall temple to show off. If a tree is heavy with good fruit, its branches hang down low near the ground,' he said. 'Our gurdwara shall be low near the ground.'

Not only was the gurdwara low outside, but Sikhs had to go down steps inside the temple as well.

At this time in India there were four classes of people – priests, soldiers, businessmen, and workers. They never mixed for their religion would not allow this. They were forbidden to eat together, or even talk together. As for marrying someone from a different class, that was completely out of the question. The Sikhs said this was wrong – they believed that all men are equal in the sight of God.

There were in India many religions – Muslim, Hindu, Buddhist, Christian, and Sikh. Guru Arjan had four great doors built in the temple to show that people of all classes and of all religions, are all equally welcome to come in to worship God.

It was Guru Arjan who gave the Sikhs their Holy Book. The third guru had already collected the hymns and poems of the first two gurus and put in some of his own. Arjan added some work of his father's, some of his own, and some of Muslim and Hindu teachers. He called the collection the *Granth Sahib*. He had the Granth Sahib placed in the centre of the Golden Temple, the most important place – too important for any person to be there.

Guru Arjan's Muslim Friends   (2 min.)

People of different religions have not always lived peacefully together. There have often been arguments and even wars. But the Sikhs have always had respect for other religions and there have been times when Sikhs and others *have* got on very well.

Guru Arjan asked a Muslim friend of his, Mian Mir, to lay the first stone of the Golden Temple. Even the Muslim Emperor, Akbar, once visited Arjan at the Golden Temple and offered to give the Guru some money to help to pay for the building work. But Guru Arjan refused. He said that the Sikhs wanted to pay for their own temple. If the Emperor had money to spare, Arjan thought he should give it to the poor people instead.

*

Guru Arjan travelled around the Punjab visiting towns and villages where Sikhs lived. He came to a place called Tarn Taran where there was no gurdwara. Arjan considered that the Sikhs of Tarn Taran ought to have their own place of worship. He looked round for a good site for them to build a gurdwara. After he had found a piece of land, some of the local Sikhs joined together to buy it from the Muslims who owned it. A price was agreed between the Sikhs and the Muslims and the sale was made.

But when the Muslims went home with the money, their wives asked them where it had come from. As soon as the wives found out that the Sikhs had paid it to build their gurdwara, they told their husbands to give it back straight away. They should not be taking money for land that was being used for the praise of God.

The next day the Muslims took the money back to the Guru Arjan. However, the Guru said that a fair price had been agreed, and the money had been paid. The Sikhs would not have the money back. In the end it was decided that the men who were building the temple should be given the money.

*

Guru Arjan's best-loved hymn is the Song of Peace:

Happiness comes from love for God;
We feel no sorrow with love for God;
The filth of pride is washed away by love for God;
We are always clean with love for God;
Listen friends: love God;
He is our life and soul;
He supports all our hearts.

(from the Sukhmani, c.1600 CE)

Guru Arjan's Death   (3 min.)

Arjan's friend, Emperor Akbar, died and Jehangir became Emperor of India. Troublemakers who did not like the Sikhs told the Emperor that Guru Arjan was preaching against the Prophet Muhammad. This was not true, but the Emperor who was a Muslim, exploded with anger and ordered the arrest of the Guru. Arjan would be freed only if he promised to stop preaching the Sikh religion and if he would pay a fine of 200,000 rupees. Arjan replied that he could never stop preaching his religion and that, if he had such a huge sum of money, he would give it to the poor people and certainly not to the Emperor.

Emperor Jehangir ordered Arjan to be tortured for these words. For three days during the month of May, which is extremely hot and dry in India, Guru Arjan was locked in a tiny prison cell with no food or water. On the fourth day he was placed in a barrel of boiling water. On the fifth day his body and head were covered with hot sand and on the sixth day he was forced to sit on a red-hot iron plate.

Never once did the Guru complain or ask for mercy. He repeated over and over to himself the name of God. This gave him the strength and the will to stand the terrible pain of his body. Even though Arjan was badly burned and very weak orders came from the Emperor that he should be ducked in cold water. This would make the burns even more painful. The guards took him from the prison at Lahore to the River Ravi. As he was led to the rushing water Arjan prayed aloud and told the Sikhs who were watching not to weep for him nor to try to get his body. Instead they should go back and praise God, for there was a new guru now – his son, Hargobind.

Arjan was roughly pushed into the river Ravi. In the strong current he was
washed away and drowned. His body was never found.

Guru Arjan was the first Sikh to die for his faith, but he was not the last.
The Indian emperors and later the British rulers of India grew more and more
frightened as the numbers and power of the Sikhs grew. But the Sikhs were to
face many more troubles before they won the right to live in peace.

*

Guru Arjan wrote these words. The way that he died shows that he meant
what he wrote:

> Join together and unite, my brothers;
> Put aside differences, love one another,
> And always remember God's name.
> Repeat his name both day and night
> And you shall not suffer at your last hour.

(from the Guru Granth Sahib, c.1600)

The Festival of Lights (Diwali)

late October/November

*Diwali, the Hindu Festival of Lights celebrating the mythological victory of
good over evil, is for many Hindus first of the New Year in Northern India.
Insides and outsides of houses, temples, and other buildings are lit up, new
clothes are worn, relatives are visited and presents, especially of sweets, are
given.*

*The third Sikh guru, Amar Das (1479–1574 CE) instituted Diwali and
Baisakhi (q.v.) as the two annual Sikh festivals. The day is also remembered as
the anniversary of the release of the sixth guru, Hargobind Rai (1595–1645 CE)
from prison. To celebrate the Guru's return to freedom in Amritsar, the people
of the city who had lit up their houses for Diwali, also illuminated the Golden
Temple, a tradition which has continued to this day. The festival follows Hindu
lines and is celebrated with gifts, lights, and fireworks.*

Guru Hargobind   (5 min.)

Hargobind was the sixth Sikh guru. He was a friend of the Muslim emperor of India, Emperor Jehangir. Although Jehangir did not like Sikhs or Hindus and often made life hard for them, he got on very well with Hargobind and often visited the eating-place at his gurdwara.

A time came when Emperor Jehangir fell ill. The best doctors in India were called for and the people prayed in the mosques for him to get well, but it was no use. No one really knew what was the matter with him. No one knew how to cure him and the Emperor grew worse.

At the Emperor's palace were many who did not like Guru Hargobind. When it was asked if there were any holy men who might pray to save the Emperor's life, a courtier named Chandu suggested that they send for Hargobind. But Chandu also cleverly put it into the Emperor's head that Guru Hargobind might be the one who had put a curse on him and made him ill in the first place. Chandu suggested that perhaps Hargobind was trying to poison him when he ate at the gurdwara. Hargobind was sent for by the Emperor's command to pray for him at the Fort of Gwalior.

Gladly Hargobind came to the fort. But when he passed through its massive gates, they slammed shut behind him and were locked. Chandu had sent a secret report to the fort that Guru Hargobind was planning to make himself the King of the Punjab. He ordered that as soon as Hargobind entered the Gwalior Fort he should be arrested and killed. The guards seized Hargobind and made ready to kill him. However, when some of the officers saw this, they stopped the orders from being carried out. Although they were Muslim soldiers of the Emperor, they were good friends of the Sikhs. So Hargobind was locked in the prison of the Gwalior Fort instead.

The days passed slowly in the dark and crowded prison. Hargobind was not alone. There were no fewer than fifty-two Indian princes already imprisoned at the fort. They were there because the Emperor was frightened that they might rise against him.

Conditions were bad – what little food was given was poor. Prisoners were not allowed outside the cells for fresh air. The place was filthy and full of rats. Hargobind continually asked the governor in charge of the fort to make things better. Day after day Hargobind asked to see the governor; day after day he demanded the same things. At last the governor grew so tired of the Guru that he did make conditions better.

As the weeks went slowly by, news came that the Emperor was getting better. At last the Emperor was cured. Guru Hargobind waited to hear he would go free. But the message never came from the Emperor's palace – the Emperor had forgotten that Hargobind was there at all.

Eventually a Muslim called Mian Mir went to see the Emperor. Mian Mir had been a friend of Hargobind's father and had helped him to build the famous Golden Temple of Amritsar. He demanded that Hargobind should be set free.

The Emperor was angry, but when he received petitions, not only from Sikhs but from other Muslims as well, he gave orders that the Guru should be set free.

When Hargobind was told the news of his release he refused to leave. He would only leave, he said, if the fifty-two Indian princes were also set free. The Emperor was furious. But then he changed his mind and decided he would play a rather nasty joke on Guru Hargobind and the princes. He said that as many princes could go free with Hargobind as could hold on to his clothes when he walked out of the fort.

Hargobind tore up the princes' coats and jackets into strips, and tied the fifty-two long ribbons of cloth to his clothes. Then walked through the gates to freedom, with an Indian prince holding on to each ribbon.

When Hargobind returned to Amritsar, it was the great feast of Diwali, the Festival of Lights. All the houses were lit up and the great Golden Temple was lit up, too. The Sikhs were delighted to see Hargobind, and remembered the ancient meaning of the festival – that good always triumphs over evil.

*

This is a prayer of Guru Gobind Singh.

God is in the water, God is in the dry land, God is in the heart.
God is in the forest, God is in the mountain, God is in the cave.
God is in the earth, God is in heaven.
He is in the tree, He is in the leaves.
He is in the earth and in the depths.

(Gobind Singh, 1666–1708)

The Birthday of Guru Nanak

late November/December

Guru Nanak Dev, the first Sikh guru and founder of the faith, was born in 1469 CE in the village of Talwandi (now in Pakistan) about 65 km from Lahore. His father was the village tax-collector and accountant and the family were high-caste Hindus. After a revelation he attempted to unite Muslims and Hindus in a

vision of one God and made four missionary journeys: east as far as Assam,
India, south to Sri Lanka, north to Tibet, and west to Mecca, Saudi Arabia.
Nanak lived at Kartarpur for many years where he built the first gurdwara and
where a small but growing community of disciples began to gather. He died at
the age of 70 in 1539 CE. There are many tales of his deep religious faith.
Nanak's own writings form part of the Sikh Holy Book, the Guru Granth Sahib
part of which is recited by devout Sikhs every morning.

The birthday of Guru Nanak is an important day for Sikhs. Guru Nanak
founded the Sikh religion in the Punjab on the borders of India and Pakistan
over 500 years ago. Each year in the Sikh gurdwaras (temples) all over the world
the Sikh Holy Book, the Guru Granth Sahib, is read without a break from
beginning to end. The reading takes two full days. Different readers take part
and the reading finishes on Guru Nanak's birthday.

Guru Nanak as a Boy   (3 min.)

Nanak was born into a wealthy Hindu family in the Punjab. In those days the
Muslims and the Hindus did not always get on very well together. But when
Nanak was a boy he was very friendly to both Hindus and Muslims.

When he was eight, Nanak had to go through a Hindu ceremony where a
sacred thread is put over the shoulder. The thread is plaited with three strands
of cotton to represent the Hindu idea of God as three beings in one. When the
holy man came to put the thread over Nanak's shoulder, the boy wouldn't let
him.

'Cotton wears out,' said Nanak. 'Instead, plait me a thread of good
thoughts for my soul:

Out of the cotton of kindness,
Plait a thread of happiness.
Tie a knot of good behaviour,
Give it a twist of truthfulness,
And make a sacred thread for your soul.'

*

There are many stories of Guru Nanak when he was a boy. Here are three of
them:

One day Nanak fell asleep in the cooling shade of a tree that grew on the
outskirts of his village. As he slept, the chief of the village went past. Several
hours later the chief came past again and stared in amazement. The sun had
moved across the sky so the shadow of the tree should have moved too.

Nanak was still sleeping in the tree's cool shade. The shade had stayed still to keep the hot sun off the young boy.

Another time Nanak was put in charge of his father's cows. Nanak forgot about the cows as he sat thinking. Left by themselves, the cows wandered off and started to eat a neighbour's crops. Unfortunately, the neighbour came by. He woke Nanak, shouting that he had let the cows trample his fields. The neighbour stormed off to complain to the chief of the village, but when the chief came the crops were perfect. They had grown back, tall and straight. Not one part of the field appeared to be trampled.

One day Nanak's father sent him to the local market with some money to buy food. He told Nanak to make sure he spent the money wisely. On the way, Nanak passed a number of hungry men. At the market he bargained hard to buy as much food as he could find and on his return he gave it all to the hungry men.

His father was furious. 'I told you to use the money wisely,' he said angrily.

'I used it wisely,' said Nanak. 'I helped the poor.'

Guru Nanak Becomes the Servant of God   (2 min.)

When Nanak grew older he went to work for a rich and powerful man who was an Afghan chief in Sultanpur. He was put in charge of the accounts. This meant he had to write in a book how much money was spent and how much money was earned. He also kept records of everything that was grown on the chief's land. Nanak was good at his job. He earned enough money for himself and his wife to live quite well.

One day Nanak was bathing in the river. One of the chief's servants was watching him from the bank. The next minute Nanak had gone. The servant looked and looked but Nanak seemed to have disappeared.

The chief was told and he sent divers to search the river bottom. Fishermen were sent for to drag their nets over about ten kilometres of the river. But Nanak was not to be found. It was presumed that he had drowned.

Three days later Nanak returned to his home. His wife was overjoyed to see him again, but she was amazed to see that he was giving away all their good food and furniture, their nice clothes and ornaments, to the poor people of the village. She understood when Nanak told her that he had seen a vision of God and had now to preach his message. He called the people of the village together, and told them:

'There is no Hindu. There is no Muslim. I am a brother to all who love God. All lovers of God are brothers together.'

Nanak sent a message to the chief saying that he could be his servant no longer. The chief understood and sent back a message asking Nanak, in the name of God, to come and see him. The chief saw that Nanak was a changed man. He begged him to be his personal adviser.

But Nanak told him:

'I have accepted the service of God. God alone will I serve. I will not serve any man or earthly ruler all my life.'

*

If I had a hundred thousand tongues and not just one
And a hundred thousand times twenty,
A hundred thousand times I'd say and say again,
There is but one God and only one.

(from the Guru Granth Sahib, *c*.1500 CE)

Guru Nanak's Travels: Guru Nanak in Mecca   (1 min.)

Nanak left the village of Sultanpur and set off with his friend, Mardana, on four great journeys to the north, south and east, and to Mecca in the west. When he reached the Ka'ba in Mecca, the holiest place of the Muslim faith, Nanak spent much time in prayer. One night Nanak fell asleep with his feet pointing towards the holy Ka'ba. A Muslim woke up Nanak with a mighty kick. He was beside himself with anger:

'How dare you sleep with your feet pointing towards the House of God!' he cried. 'It is a shocking insult to Allah.'

'If I am insulting Allah by pointing my feet towards His house,' said Nanak calmly, 'Show me a place where I can point them without insulting God. God is everywhere.'

Guru Nanak and the Poor Carpenter   (3 min.)

On his travels with Mardana, Nanak came to a city where he was now well known. Instead of staying at the house of some rich person, Nanak chose to knock at the door of a tiny ramshackle cottage that belonged to a poor but hard-working carpenter. The carpenter was amazed that the famous preacher should call at his house but he made him welcome. The poor man had hardly any food but what he had he gladly gave to Nanak and Mardana. The carpenter had only a tumbledown uncomfortable bed, but this too he gave to Nanak for the night.

In the morning Nanak asked the carpenter to leave him alone in the cottage for a short while. No sooner had the carpenter and Mardana gone outside, when they heard dreadful crashings and bangings and saw through the window that Nanak was smashing up all the furniture.

'I have nothing worth having,' said the poor man, 'but that is all I have.'

'Don't worry,' answered Mardana. 'Guru Nanak seems to do some strange things, but he always has a very good reason.'

Then Nanak came outside the cottage with a brand from the fire and set fire to the wooden house. The carpenter watched silently, but with tears in his eyes as his small cottage burned down.

'Life is often unkind,' said Nanak. 'Why should a kind and generous man like this carpenter live a life of misery and hardship when there are rich and undeserving people living not far away?'

Nanak led the carpenter into the centre of the town where many people crowded to see him. Ordinary people gave the famous Guru a few pence or some food and the rich sent their servants with gifts. As evening came the Guru had collected an enormous pile of presents and money from the townsfolk which he gave to the carpenter:

'You need these gifts more than I ever shall,' he said. 'Buy yourself a new house, set yourself up in business and always be grateful to God.'

Guru Nanak and the Leper   (3 min.)

Guru Nanak came to a village called Dipalpur. As night was closing in he asked a passer-by where he could stay. The villager told him to knock on the door of Nuri's house. Nanak found the house and when the door was opened saw at once that Nuri was a leper.

Nanak did not jump back in horror as others might have done. Leprosy is a dreadful disease which eats away parts of a person's body. In those days lepers suffered terribly as no one would come near them for fear of catching the disease. Instead he said gently,

'I have been told I might stay at your house.'

'Some one has been playing a nasty joke on us both,' replied Nuri. 'As you can see I am a leper. No one will come near me; people make fun of me – I am a hated man.'

'Your body is full of pain and suffering,' replied Nanak, 'but I can see that your soul is good. You have the love of God within you. You shall be cured of your disease. Your body shall be as pure as your soul.'

And as Nanak said, Nuri was cured of the terrible disease from which he had suffered for so long.

*

After many years Guru Nanak returned home from his travels. He lived in the town of Kartarpur where he built the very first Sikh gurdwara. Nanak wrote many hymns and his old friend, Mardana, wrote the music which he played on the rabaab, a stringed instrument invented by the Guru. Hindus and Muslims came from miles around to join in. Many came to live at Kartarpur so that they could hear Nanak teaching. These followers were called Nanak's disciples and the Punjabi word for disciples is 'Sikhs'. There are now over 8,000,000 Sikhs in India and Pakistan and in many other countries of the world including Britain.

*

Many of Guru Nanak's prayers and hymns are to be found in the Sikh holy book, the Guru Granth Sahib. Here are two of them:

Just as there is a scent in a flower
And reflection in a mirror,
So God is in you.
Find him in your heart.

The sun is always the same,
But there are many seasons;
So God can be found in many different ways.

*

Saints or sinners aren't made by what they *say*;
The things they *do* decide what they become;
You sow the seeds and reap the harvest from them;
Be saved or be reborn again and again.

(from the Guru Granth Sahib, *c*.1500 CE)

The Martyrdom of Guru Tegh Bahadur

December

Departing from the policy of toleration of other religious groups taken by previous Mughal emperors, Aurangzeb, a Muslim, began an active policy of forcing Sikhs and Hindus within his empire (northern India) to accept Islam. The seventh guru, Har Rai (1630–1661 CE) and his young son, the eighth, Har Krishen (1656–1664 CE) were not involved in confrontations with the Emperor.

But Tegh Bahadur (1621–1675 CE) was. However, Tegh Bahadur continued to work around the Punjab standing against the Emperor on behalf of Sikhs and Hindus alike. He was executed in 1675, the succession passing to his son, Gobind Rai.

The Martyrdom of Guru Tegh Bahadur   (9 min.)

Many Sikhs had suffered for their religion. One of their leaders, Guru Arjan, had died for it. Then an Emperor came to power who wanted everyone else in India to be Muslim like himself. If they did not do as he said, he punished them. Sikhs had found their gurdwaras destroyed by the Emperor's soldiers. Sikh pilgrims travelling to the holy city of Amritsar had found they now had to pay before they could enter. Sikhs began to find it impossible to get government jobs. Not only did Emperor Aurangzeb see to it that the Sikhs suffered, he made sure that the Hindus suffered too.

The leader of the Sikhs was now Guru Tegh Bahadur who decided that he should go round the Punjab visiting the Sikh villages, letting them know that the Guru still cared for them, and that if they suffered from the Emperor's persecution, he suffered too. The Guru walked mile after mile and visited hundreds of villages and spoke to thousands of people. The more he travelled and the more he preached, the angrier Emperor Aurangzeb became.

But the Emperor was not Tegh Bahadur's only enemy. Tegh Bahadur had a nephew called Dhirmal. Dhirmal was a jealous man. Perhaps he wanted to be famous like his uncle.

There was a time when Dhirmal paid some thieves to go to Tegh Bahadur's house while he was out to steal anything worth taking and smash anything that wasn't. While the thieves were there, Tegh Bahadur came home. A shot was fired and the Guru was hit in the shoulder. The thieves escaped. It was not long before the Sikhs hunted them down and dragged them and Dhirmal back before the Guru. Instead of punishing them Tegh Bahadur simply smiled, forgave them, and set them free.

Tegh Bahadur's worst enemy was the Emperor Aurangzeb, a man so cruel that he had murdered his own two brothers and starved his father to death. Aurangzeb sent his soldiers throughout the country forcing everyone to become a Muslim. Many Sikhs and Hindus were killed for refusing. In the hills of Kashmir some Hindus had been ordered by the governor to become Muslims. They were honest men who would not change their religion just because they had been told to – so their lives were in danger. They escaped from Kashmir and travelled to the town of Anandpur in the Punjab where Guru Tegh Bahadur lived. There they begged him to give them protection.

They knew that Sikhs cared for people of other religions as well as their own, so they weren't afraid to ask for help.

After the Hindus had begged for Tegh Bahadur's help, the Guru sat at home wondering what he ought to do. His nine year old son, Gobind Rai was playing in the same room.

'What's the matter, Father? You seem troubled.'

'Well, my son, maybe you're too young to understand the cruelty of others, but the Emperor has threatened to kill these people if they do not change their religion. Something will have to be done. They need someone who is not only brave, but also a man of God, good and holy, to protect them from the Emperor's wickedness.'

'Well, I know a man like that,' cried Gobind Rai. 'My father, it is you! You are good and holy, a man of God, and you are not afraid of the Emperor.'

The Guru realised what he must do. He sent a message to the Emperor saying that if he could persuade the leader of the Sikhs to change his religion, then not only would these Kashmiri Hindus change, but the whole of India would be converted too.

The Emperor was delighted. He sent for the Guru immediately. But his delight was soon turned to anger and his anger became rage as he heard what Tegh Bahadur had to say:

'You cannot *force* people to change what they believe. Even the great Prophet Muhammad never did that. Men must believe in God and worship him in any way they think is right. Are you so proud that you think you can make people believe the same as you? Only God can do that. But God does not choose to. He has made the world like a garden full of different flowers, with many colours and perfumes. The world is better like this with people living in ways that suit them best.'

The Emperor's rage turned to fury and he ordered his soldiers to take the Guru away and torture him until he changed his views. Tegh Bahadur was locked in a very tiny cage and was gradually starved. Each day he was asked if he would give up the Sikh religion. Each day the answer was the same – no. He became thin and weak from lack of food and water, and at last the Emperor, unable to break his spirit, lost his patience and signed his death warrant. For the last time he was asked if he would change his religion.

'I will always be a Sikh. Never will I give up my faith for fear of death,' he said.

As he was led to the place of execution, the Guru repeated one of Guru Nanak's prayers. He was made to kneel down by a banyan tree as the executioner raised his great sword.

'Waheguru, waheguru; O wonderful Lord,' he cried out. Then the great sword sliced down.

Immediately a fierce storm broke and the heavy rain forced the soldiers to shelter and leave the beheaded body beside the tree. Secretly two Sikhs crept out into the rain. The one took the Guru's body back to his own house and so that the Emperor would find no trace of it, he burned down his house with the body inside. The other took the Guru's head and set out for Anandpur where the Guru's son, Gobind Rai, was to become the tenth guru.

When the rain had stopped the soldiers came to collect the body to prove to the Emperor that the Guru was dead. There was no body there. Just a note fastened to the banyan tree, which read:

'He gave his head, but not his faith.'

*

Guru Tegh Bahadur was the second Sikh guru to die for his beliefs. What is most surprising, perhaps, is that he died, not because he was protecting his own followers, but Hindus. He must have remembered the words of the first guru, Nanak:

'There is no Hindu. There is no Muslim. I am a brother to all lovers of God.'

Like other Sikh gurus, Guru Tegh Bahadur wrote poems, hymns, and prayers to teach the Sikhs their religion:

Don't count the things you own,
Or money, or your wealth in land;
Not one of these can help you.
God gave you a body, wealth and a home,
So why not give him praises?
He helps the poor, the low and those afraid;
He is always near, the helper of the helpless.
God is the giver of all things good,
    and only God;
Repeat his name;
It is the only way you will be saved.

(from the Slokas of Guru Tegh Bahadur, c.1650 CE)

Bibliography

If this book is to be used as a calendar of festivals it is obviously necessary to know the dates when the festivals will occur. A calendar with brief and useful notes on each festival is published annually in July.

Calendar of Religious Festivals
ed. Desmond F. Brennan for the SHAP Working Party.
Published by Commission for Racial Equality, Elliot House, 10–12 Allington St, London SW1E 5EH.
Also available from: SHAP,
7 Alderbrook Rd, Solihull,
West Midlands, B91 1NH.

I found the following two teachers' resource books very useful. Each has a very thorough bibliography and is full of ideas for use in assembly as well as in RE teaching.

Living Together: A Teachers' Handbook of Suggestions for Religious Education
City of Birmingham Education Department, 1975 (and its Supplement, 1981).
From Chief Education Officer,
Margaret St, Birmingham B3 3BU.

Religion in the Multi-Faith School
ed. W. O. Cole, Bradford Educational Services Committee/Yorkshire Committee for Community Relations 1973.
Available from YCCR, Charlton House, Hunslet Rd, Leeds LS10 1EH.

Three multi-faith books for teachers:

A Book of World Religions
E. G. Parrinder, Hulton Educational Publications, 1965.

How Others See Life. Schools Council RE in Secondary Schools Project
Hart-Davis Educational, 1977.

Man and his Gods: Encyclopaedia of the World's Religions ed. E. G. Parrinder, Hamlyn, 1971.

Some series for children, the first two being particularly useful for younger children:

The Way of Series:
The Buddha, the Hindu, the Jew, the Muslim, the Sikh Hulton Educational, 1972.

Our Friends Series:
Muslim, Christian, Hindu, Jewish, Sikh, Buddhist 1978. National Christian Education Council, Denholm House Press, Redhill, Surrey.

A Family in Britain Series:
Hindu, Jewish, Muslim, Sikh, West Indian Religious Education Press, 1972/73.

Understanding Your Neighbour Series:
Jewish, Muslim, Hindu, Sikh Lutterworth, 1976.

Thinking About Series:
Buddhism, Christianity, Hinduism, Islam, Judaism, Sikhism Lutterworth, 1971.

The following books will prove very useful because, by and large, they give a view from the inside of the religions concerned:

The Story of the Buddha (for children)
The Association of Buddhist Women in the UK, London Buddhist Vihara, 5 Heathfield Gardens, London W4 4JU.

Chinese Myths and Fantasies Cyril Birch, Oxford University Press, 1961.

Confucius Betty Kelen, Sheldon Press, 1971.

The Christian Calendar
L. W. Cowrie and J. S. Gummer.
Weidenfeld and Nicolson, 1974.

The Children's Bible
ed. David L. Edwards, from the Good News Bible.
Collins, 1978.

Indian Tales and Legends J. E. B. Gray, Oxford University Press, 1961.

193

The Legend of Krishna
Nigel Frith, Abacus, 1975.

Round the Year ed. L. Barwell and
Showensohn, 1966. Jewish National
Fund, 4–12 Regent St, London SW1.

The Complete Festival Service
N. Mindel, Chinuch, 1956.

Islam: Beliefs and Teachings
Ghulam Sarwar, 1969. The Muslim
Educational Trust, 130 Stroud Green
Rd, London N4 3RZ.

First, Second and Third Primers of Islam
The Muslim Educational Trust,
1969/1973.

Islamic Correspondence Course
Minarets House, 9 Leslie Park Rd.,
Croydon, Surrey, CRO 6TN.

Guru Nanak (for children) G. S. Sidhu,
G. S. Sivia and Kirpal Singh Rai, 1969.
The Sikh Missionary Society, 10
Featherstone Rd, Southall, Middlesex

The Guru's Way (for children), (as above)
1970.

In the Guru's Footsteps (as above) 1971.

The Saint-Soldier (as above) 1974.

From the following (and others) I have
adapted my quotations at the end of each
story. Teachers may be interested to see the
translations and make their own adaptations
or selection:

The Many Faces of Religion
ed. S. Dicks, Ginn, 1973.

Sacred Books of the World
A. C. Bouquet, Penguin, 1954.

*With One Voice: Prayers and Thoughts
from World Religions* Sid G. Hedges,
Religious Education Press, 1970.

The Dhammapada trans. Juan Mascaro,
Penguin, 1973.

The Book of Songs trans. Arthur Waley,
Grove Press, New York, 1937.

The New English Bible with Apocrypha
Oxford University Press/Cambridge
University Press, 1961/1970.

The Book of Common Prayer
Cambridge University Press, 1922.

The Parish Missal C. Goodlifefe Neale,
Birmingham, 1966.

The Methodist Hymn Book
The Methodist Publishing House, 1933.

The Authorized Version of the Bible
The British and Foreign Bible Society,
1954.

*Liturgies Eastern and Western. Volume 1:
Eastern Liturgies* ed. F. E. Brightman,
Oxford University Press, 1896.

The Festal Menaion trans. Mother Mary
and Archimandrite Kallistos Ware,
Faber and Faber, 1969.

Service of the Synagogue
ed. Herbert M. Adler, George Routledge
and Sons, 1904.

The Holy Qur'an trans. A. Yusuf Ali,
Dar Al Arabia, Beirut, 1968.

Hymns of Guru Nanak
trans. Khushwant Singh, Orient
Longmans, New Delhi, 1969.

Selections from the Holy Granth
Gurbachan Singh Talib, Vikas
Publishing House, Delhi, 1975.

*Selections from the Sacred Writing of the
Sikhs* George Allen and Unwin, 1960.

Sri Guru Granth Sahib
trans. Gopal Singh, Gur Das Kapur
and Sons, Delhi, 1960.

I have also consulted the following books to a
greater or lesser degree:

The Encyclopaedia of Islam Luzac, 1960.

Encyclopaedia Judaica K. Keter
Publishing House, Jerusalem, 1972.

*New Larousse Encyclopaedia of
Mythology* Hamlyn, 1959.

A Manual of Hadith
Maulana Muhammad Ali, Curzon
Press, 1944.

Comparative Religion A. C. Bouquet,
Penguin, 1941/1962.

Mahabharata retold by William Buck, University of California Press, Berkeley, 1973.

The Sikhs – their Religious Beliefs and Practices W. O. Cole and Piara Singh Sambhi, Routledge and Kegan Paul, 1978.

World Religions: a Handbook for Teachers ed. W. O. Cole, Commission for Racial Equality/SHAP Working Party, 1977.

The Life of Muhammad trans. of Ishaq's Sirat Rasul Allah by A. Guillaume, Oxford University Press, 1955.

East Comes West ed. P. Holroyde, Commission for Racial Equality, 1974.

Buddhism Christmas Humphreys, Penguin, 1951.

Indian Mythology Veronica Ions, Hamlyn, 1967.

Myths and Legends of India Veronica Ions, Hamlyn, 1970.

How to Teach Buddhism to Children Helmuth Klar, Buddhist Publication Society, Kandy, Sri Lanka, 1975.

The Buddha Trevor Ling, Maurice Temple Smith, 1973.

Buddhism Trevor Ling, Ward Lock Educational, 1970.

The Sikhs of the Punjab W. H. McLeod, Oriel Press, 1968.

The World's Living Religions Geoffrey Parrinder, Pan, 1964.

What the Buddha Taught Walpola Rahula, Gordon Fraser, Bedford, 1959.

Hinduism K. M. Sen, Penguin, 1961.

Life of Muhammad Abdul Siddiqui, Islamic Publications, Lahore, Pakistan, 1969.

Guru Nanak and the Message of Peace Parkash Singh, Singh Brothers, Amritsar, India, 1969.

Guru Nanak, Founder of Sikhism Trilochan Singh, Gurdwara Parbandhak Committee, Delhi, 1969.

Confucius D. Howard Smith, Maurice Temple Smith, 1973.

Buddhism in a Nutshell Naroda Thera, Buddhist Publication Society, Kandy, 1975.

Epics, Myths and Legends of India P. Thomas, D. B. Taraporevala and Sons, Bombay, 1973.

The Majesty That was Islam: the Islamic World 661–1100 W. Montgomery Watt, Sidgwick and Jackson, 1974.

Confucius and Confucianism Richard Wilhelm, trans. George and Annina Danton, 1931.

Appendix

The Stories in Historical Order

Not all of the stories can be fitted into this pattern, but those that make a more or less continuous historical narrative are listed here.

Buddhism: The Story of the Buddha

The Early Life of Prince Siddhartha	Birthday of Buddha Sakyamuni
The Young Prince Siddhartha	The Day of Enlightenment
Buddha, the Enlightened One	Vesakha
The Buddha and the Five Hermits	The Day of the Turning of the Wheel of the Law
The Buddha's First Sermon	
Devadatta Tries to Kill the Buddha	The Death of the Buddha Day
Devadatta Tries to Kill the Buddha	Vesakha
King Ajatasatru Becomes a Buddhist	The Day of the Turning of the Wheel of the Law
Assalayana Tries to Catch the Buddha out	Vesakha
The Buddha Converts his Family to Buddhism	The Day of Enlightenment
The Death of the Buddha	The Day of the Death of the Buddha
A Small Boy's Gift	Poson
King Ashoka Becomes a Buddhist	Poson

Christianity: The Story of Jesus

The Angel Gabriel Visits Mary	Lady Day
The Birth of John the Baptist	Advent
The Birth of Jesus	Christmas
The Baptism of Jesus	Shrove Tuesday
Jesus is Tempted by the Devil	Ash Wednesday
Andrew Becomes a Disciple of Jesus	St. Andrew's Day
The Feeding of Five Thousand People	St. Andrew's Day
The Death of John the Baptist	The Feast Day of John the Baptist
Jesus's Entry into Jerusalem	Palm Sunday
Jesus's Last Supper with his Disciples	Maundy Thursday
The Death of Jesus	Good Friday
The Resurrection of Jesus	Easter Sunday
Jesus and Peter	Ascension Day
Jesus Ascends into Heaven	Ascension Day
Jesus's Disciples Receive the Holy Spirit	Whitsun

196

Hinduism: The Story of Rama

Rama and Sita Leave the Kingdom	Rama's Birthday
Rama Defeats the Demon Ravana	The Ten Days
Rama and Sita Return	The Festival of Lights

Hinduism: The Story of Krishna

The Birth of Krishna	The Birthday of Krishna
Lord Krishna and the Priests' Wives	The Festival of Colour
Krishna and the Village Girls	The Festival of Colour
Krishna Kills the Demon Kansa	The Festival of Colour

Judaism: Stories of the Jews

Abraham Prepares to Sacrifice Isaac	New Year
The Jews Leave Egypt	The Passover
Moses and the Israelites in the Desert	The Feast of Tabernacles
The Ten Commandments	The Feast of Weeks
The Death of Moses	The Rejoicing of the Law
The Story of Ruth	The Feast of Weeks
King David – David is Anointed	The Feast of Weeks
David and Goliath	The Feast of Weeks
David and Saul	The Feast of Weeks
Jonah and the Whale	The Day of Atonement
Jonah in Nineveh	The Day of Atonement
Nebuchadrezzar Destroys Jerusalem	The Fast of 9 Av
The Jews Return from Babylon	The Fast of 9 Av
Esther the Jewess Becomes Queen of Persia	The Fast of Esther
Esther Saves the Persian Jews	Lots
Judas Maccabaeus Restores the Temple	The Festival of Lights
The Romans Destroy Jerusalem	The Fast of 9 Av

Islam: The Story of Muhammad

The Birth and Early Life of Muhammad	Prophet's Day
Muhammad is Given the Holy Qur'an	Ramadan
Muhammad's Flight from Mecca	New Year

Sikhism: The Stories of the Gurus

Guru Nanak as a Boy	The Birthday of Guru Nanak
Guru Nanak Becomes the Servant of God	The Birthday of Guru Nanak
Guru Nanak's Travels	The Birthday of Guru Nanak
Guru Nanak and the Poor Carpenter	The Birthday of Guru Nanak
Guru Nanak and the Leper	The Birthday of Guru Nanak

Guru Arjan Builds the Golden Temple	The Martyrdom of Guru Arjan Dev
Guru Arjan's Muslim Friends	The Martyrdom of Guru Arjan Dev
The Death of Guru Arjan	The Martyrdom of Guru Arjan Dev
Guru Hargobind	The Festival of Lights
The Martyrdom of Guru Tegh Bahadur	The Martyrdom of Guru Tegh Bahadur
Gobind Rai Becomes the Last Sikh Guru	The Birthday of Guru Gobind Singh
The Founding of the Army of Soldier-Saints	New Year
Guru Gobind Singh and the Water Carrier	The Birthday of Guru Gobind Singh
Guru Gobind Singh Finds a True Sikh	The Birthday of Guru Gobind Singh
The Sikh Holy Book	The Birthday of Guru Gobind Singh